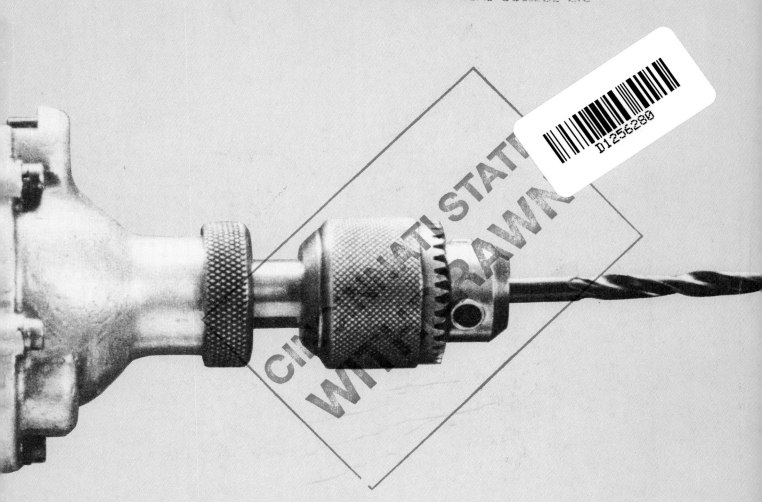

ERGONOMIC TOOLS IN OUR TIME

An Atlas Copco know-how publication

The man behind the machine remains the same.
The photos on the inside and rear cover show
the contrast in design between an early model
power drill and the latest state-of-the art modern
counterpart.

Managing Editor: Bo Lindqvist
Authors: Bo Lindqvist, Erik Ahlberg,
  Lars Skogsberg
Layout: Hellmans, Stockholm
Drawings: Gunnar Säfsund
Photo contributions: Lars Lindgren,
  Christian Stark

Printed by TR Tryck. Stockholm 1986.
A know-how production from Atlas Copco

ISBN 91-7810-535-8

Atlas Copco Tools Printed Matter
No 9833 8150 01

ergoline

Preface

Modern, high-efficiency power tools used in today's industries have not appeared by chance. They are the result of a long and continuous process of research and development extending over many decades. Research and development carried out hand-in-hand in collaboration with end-users and medical expertise.

The demands placed by end-users on the products supplied by tool manufacturers are constantly increasing and changing, not only towards high work output but also to conform to higher levels of safety, ergonomics and industrial hygiene conditions and applications. These demands are centered nowadays on low noise levels, minimum vibration, effective dust control, low weight, compact design and high-performance capability. This has caused something of a dilemma for tool designers and compelled them to become highly creative and innovative to meet such demands.

Proposed solutions must be kept within strict economic limitations in order to remain competitive. Quantification of related parameters, in turn, dictates widespread cooperation in the formation and establishment of current and future international standards, to eliminate the growth of trade barriers.

A well-designed tool can provide a number of important advantages immediately noticeable to management. Namely, increased productivity on a continuous basis, improved quality of the end-product and reduced absenteeism among the labour force for health reasons.

The intention of this book is to explain how a good knowledge of ergonomics can be used for creating efficient and user-friendly hand-held tools.

Jan Holdo
Senior Vice President technology

Contents

HOW TO DESIGN
tool handles and triggers
for low physical load

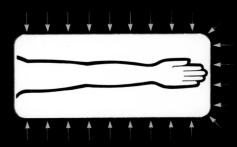

HOW TO DESIGN
tool handles and triggers for low physical load *by Bo Lindqvist*

HOW TO DESIGN
tool handles and triggers for low physical load

Compressed air-powered hand-held tools are widely used within a broad spectrum of different industries.

The combination of precision workmanship and the high power of modern hand-held tools enables us to carry out complicated tasks many times faster than ever before. A well designed workplace equipped with carefully chosen tools often results in high productivity.

A sub-standard workplace with ill-chosen tools often leads to low productivity and, even worse, the operator employed in this environment over a long period of time can develop health problems and symptoms of injury.

This publication describes the Atlas Copco approach to ergonomics in the design of hand-held tools.

The design of different types of hand-held tools obviously depends on the type of work the tool will be required to do, e.g. grinding, nutrunning, etc. It should also be equally obvious that the tool should be designed in such a way that it is adapted to the limitations of the human physique.

When craftsmen made their own tools, this adaptation became an expression of professional skills.

When the farmer taught his son to manufacture axes, spades, and so on, often according to measurements relating directly to those parts of the body which were of importance to create an efficient system of the man and the tool. It was a transfer of knowledge which had taken many generations to develop.

Our modern tools are manufactured in large series. They are much more effective than the tools of old, but also more technically complicated. The technical development of machines has been a full time occupation for many manufacturers.

Atlas Copco has also been working intensively in this area, but, at the same time, we have also given considerable attention to integration of ergonomics.

Before we go further into the actual design of our tools, it would be appropriate to give some thought to the most important factors that influence the design of a hand tool.

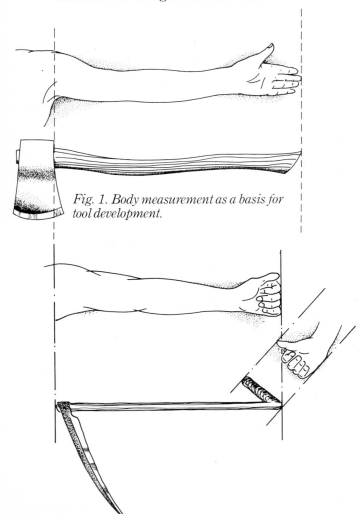

Fig. 1. Body measurement as a basis for tool development.

Static and dynamic work

When we talk about heavy manual labour, we usually mean work which engages large muscle groups of the body resulting in increased heart beat and respiration, body temperature, and so forth.

A person in good physical condition will experience this type of "load" as positive — he feels that he is actually doing something. Many people cycle or jog in their spare time and experience exercise in the same way.

But it can be an entirely different experience if local groups of muscles, in the arms and hands, for example, are subjected to high physical loads, particularly if the loads are of a static nature.

It is not unusual for older people to be forced to give up their jobs simply because one single aspect of their task requires high forces. For an observer, these isolated loads can be difficult to discover. The forces involved may even be low, but may exert a heavy load on the small muscles. In such a case, it may even be hard for the worker to pin-point which aspect of the work produces the heaviest load, and prolonged labour under these conditions can lead to injury and sometimes even handicap.

With dynamic loads over a long period of time, a job should not produce a load on the individual in excess of 40% of his/her maximum capability. This can be measured, for example, in terms of maximum oxygen intake capability when large muscle groups are used.

It is seldom that a job "only" involves dynamic work (cycling) without imposing lengthy static loads on smaller groups of muscles.

The subjective experience of a job is based on both static and dynamic loads. In many cases, the static loads dominate the experience in terms of fatique when we work with our arms and hands.

Static load imposed on muscles should not exceed 10% of the maximum static load in order to avoid a gradual exhaustion of the muscles.

A job involving both static and dynamic loads becomes extremely complicated from a physiological point of view. The dynamic load resulting in increased blood circulation helps to dissolve respiratory products caused by static loads, and even high, intermittent static loads have the same effect. Human beings are able to control this process and achieve an optimal balance by employing a working method that feels "right".

If we design the working environment in such a way that the possibility for self-determination is lost, we are laying the foundation for disatisfaction, and perhaps also injury to health. Controlling the situation is often an unconscious process which results in complaints which are unspecific and therefore difficult to remedy. A good hand tool should be

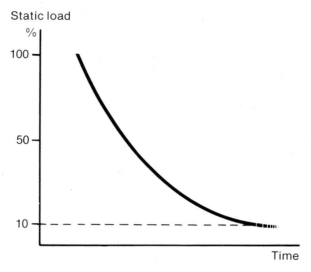

Fig. 2. Different relative static loads in relation to the time factor.

designed in such a way that an optimal balance between static and dynamic loads is spontaneously experienced, because the methods engineer designing the workplace is seldom aware of the forces which are later imposed on the body during physical labour.

Feed forces

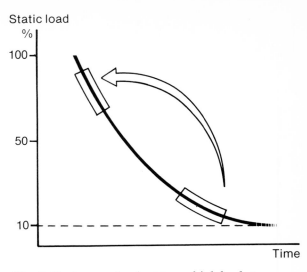

Fig. 3. *Preference of a short term, high load at capacity limit.*

When drilling, for example, the feed force is a function of the drill diameter and the drilling speed. The torque needed depends on the drill diameter as well as drill speed.

In theory, the manufacturer can limit the torque of the tool so that it cuts out if the operator attempts to attain such high penetration speed that the feed force produces excessive static loads on the hand-forearm system.

This is not done, however, as such a machine would take longer to drill a given hole.

A short term, high load at the limit of capacity, is preferable to a long-term low load at the limit of capacity. As a result, manufacturers try to make the machine as powerful as possible within a given volume and weight.

This can lead to high momentary surface pressure between the hand and the tool, which places demands on tool design. We will return to this aspect later on. The physical load to which people are exposed, when drilling, for example, depends on the required hole diameters, hole depth and number of holes per unit of time, and is seldom limited by the tool.

If it is still necessary to attain high feed forces during short periods we do this in the easiest possible way by creating downward pressure on the workpiece, whereby a great deal of body weight can be exploited. Working above shoulder height is extremely tiring, and should,

if possible, be avoided. The amount of available feed force in the horizontal plane depends on the friction against the floor as well as the body weight. One way of increasing this force is to create a counter force by using the free hand to pull at something close to the drill hole.

When grinding, the feed forces are considerably less than with drilling, or, for instance chipping. Grinding often takes place for long periods. Co-operation between tool and grinding wheel suppliers has led to wheels with optimal material removal capacity and wear in addition to a feed force that is acceptable to the operator. The feed force in a process gives a torque load on the tool which corresponds to a machine speed that is optimal for the grinding process. In other words, a continuous interaction between man, machine, and process.

Before we explore the way we design our tools in order to obtain the best possible transmission of feed force, we should first make a general study of the hand-forearm system.

Hand-arm system

From a technical point of view, the hand-arm system is a fantastic design. It gives us the possibility to carry out such precision work as writing with a pen or manual work such as when we use a saw or hammer.

The hand also functions as a vital sensory organ through touch which supplies the brain with information on the shape of an object, its surface structure, consistency, and location — all essential when working with material concealed from the eye.

The skeleton

A ball joint in the shoulder gives the upper arm bone great manoeuvrability in relation to the body.

In the elbow, the upper arm (a) Fig. 4 and the two bones of the lower arm the Ulna (c) and the Radius (b) meet. In the upper part of the elbow there is a semi-circular shaped notch connected to a cylinder-shaped joint on the upper arm bone, i.e. a hinge that controls the movements of the upper and lower arm.

The Ulna is attached to the upper arm by a hinge joint and the Radius by a ball joint. Between the Ulna and the Radius in the elbow there is also a joint, so when the lower arm is twisted, the Radius can revolve around the

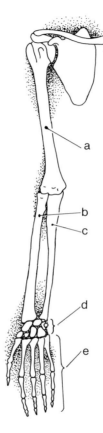

Fig. 4.

Ulna. Four of the eight bones in the wrist (d) form the radiocarpal joint which is an egg joint allowing for bending and stretching as well as sideways bending. In the next joint, the mediocarpal joint, the other four bones are connected to the lower four carpal bones. Manoeuvrability in the radiocarpal joint is approximately twice that of the mediocarpal joint. The carpal bones are held together by ligaments forming two arches, concave against the palm of the hand. Together with strong strips of connective tissue on the inside of the wrist this forms the so-called carpal tunnel.

The joints of the fingers (e) include ball joints which are stabilised at the sides by ligaments. The thumb is joined by a saddle joint which allows movement in four directions. The joint is stabilised by its muscles.

Muscles

A large number of muscles control the complex movements of the hand-arm system. The muscles of the forearm are many and lie in several layers.

Muscles which stabilize the wrist
In the outer layer are those muscles which stabilize the wrist. Fig 5 shows the right forearm as the reader sees his or her hand with the palm facing upwards. Three muscles are attached to the lower, inner part of the upper arm bone. The picture also shows attachment points along the wrist. Fig 6 shows the back of the hand with the forearm twisted clockwise. Three muscles are attached to the lower, outer

11

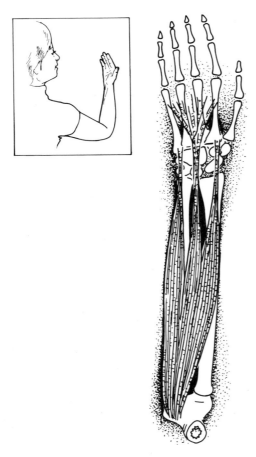

Fig. 5. Forearm muscles stabilizing the wrist.

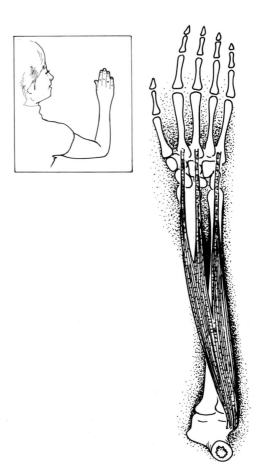

Fig. 6. Forearm muscles stabilizing the wrist.

knuckle (epicondyle) of the upper arm, and in the other end the tendons are attached to three of the middle bones (Metacarpus). These six muscles can bend the hand forwards, backwards and sideways.

From the inner epicondyle and lower arm bones start the muscles that bend the fingers Fig 7. From the outer epicondyle and the lower arm bones start the muscles that stretch the fingers Fig 8.

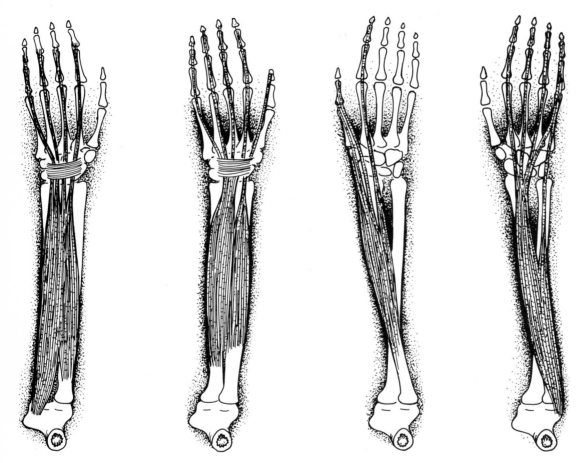

Fig. 7. Forearm muscles clenching the fingers.

Fig. 8. Forearm muscles opening the fingers.

There are four small muscles which control precision movements of the thumb and three small muscles which control movements of the little finger.

The central muscle group in the hand consists of eleven small muscles situated in the palm, mostly in the spaces between the bones of the hand. These small muscles enable us to spread our fingers and make precision movements.

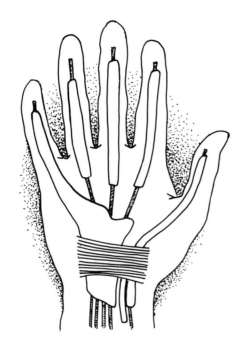

Tendon sheaths in the palm of the hand.

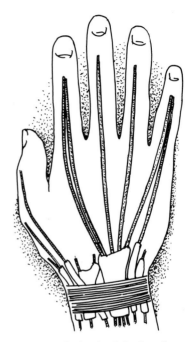

Tendon sheaths on the back of the hand.

The tendon sheaths of the hand

The muscle ends are tendons which are mostly attached to the skeleton. In the palm of the hand there are a number of tendons which all pass the wrist through a tunnel created by the Carpal bones. These form an arch and a strong connective strip of tissue.

In order for the tendons to retain their positions when the muscles contract, and to be able to move with a minimum of friction, they move in tendon sheaths. These are tubes fixed by surrounding tissue and which have an extremely well lubricated inner lining. Tendon sheaths are also located on the back of the hand near the wrist.

14

Nerves

The signals for contractions of the muscles and the sense of feeling are carried via three nerves in the hand-arm system. One runs along the Radius bone and is therefore called nervus radialis (R). One runs between the lower arm bones and is called nervus medianus (M). One runs along the Ulnaris and is called nervus ulnaris (U). The latter passes the elbow unprotected behind the inner nodule on the lower part of the upper arm. When the nervus ulnaris is struck, it produces the so-called 'knocked funny bone' sensation.

The nervus medianus passes through the carpal tunnel together with the tendon sheaths of the finger-bending tendons on the inside of the hand. This can cause a great deal of discomfort which we will deal with under the heading The Carpal Tunnel Syndrome.

The nervus ulnaris continues on the surface on the inside of the wrist. If we use the palm of the hand and wrist to hammer a workpiece into position, for example, the nerve may become damaged, resulting in numbness on the side of the hand near the little finger. The symptom is normally only temporary and subsides once the injured person becomes aware of the cause and stops the practice.

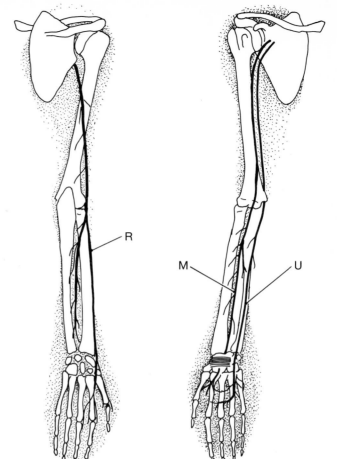

Primary nerves control the hand and arm.

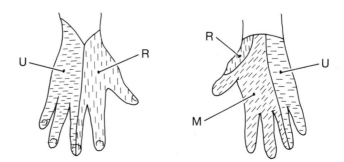

Main parts of the hand affected by these nerves.

Tool design

We have previously dealt with feed forces and the length of time these can theoretically affect a group of muscles.

A good tool design will minimize the extent of the effect of feed force on the different muscle groups, as well as transmit the force from hand to machine without causing injury. There is an optimal working position of the tool and the hand-arm system, and every deviation from this is detrimental.

Every practically inclined person realizes that there are an infinite number of working positions for most jobs, and it may therefore seem somewhat limited to merely study one optimal position. However, the aim here is to try and define those working positions which deviate most from the optimal position — those that can lead to occupational injury. Let us therefore study a number of different handles and grips which have been developed over the years.

The bow handle
About 100 years ago, machines were developed

Use of a bow grip on an Atlas Copco tool dates back to 1893.

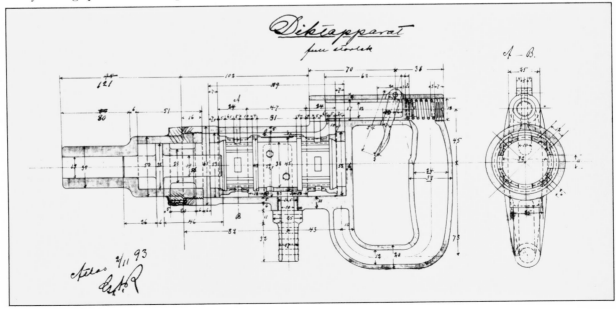

for riveting steel structures. The work required high feed forces. In all likelihood the bow grip originates from the closed handle of the spade. The handle can be either closed or open and is extremely good for transmitting high feed forces. The forces are transmitted via the groups of muscles between the thumb and little finger.

The oldest remaining drawing of an Atlas Copco hand tool is a machine equipped with a closed bow handle from 1893.

The advantage of this type of handle is that the feed force can be transmitted to the tool without creating torque in the wrist.

This presupposes that the force via the forearm, and the reaction force from the tool, interact in line.

A high grip or low grip on the tool handle gives rise to torque load with different directions in the wrist.

High feed forces often mean that all the stabilizing muscles of the wrist are engaged, which is why a further increase in the load on these muscles due to a superimposed torque is undesirable. In general, the bow handle enables the torque to be minimized.

Today, the bow handle can be found on our chipping and riveting hammers, at least on the largest models which require high feed forces, or on the smaller machines where the length of the tool is not important for performance.

The pistol handle

The demand for shorter tools for better accessibility has prompted the design of other

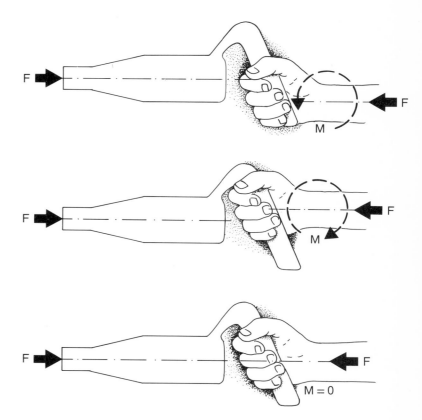

A straight line from the end of the tool to the forearm is the ideal.

types of handles.

The pistol handle was developed, for example, from the bow handle, which you can easily see from the development of our drills.

The drill BR 4 from 1915 (see page 18) was driven by a piston motor. The RAB 3, from 1930 had been equipped with a vane motor. This motor was more compact and required less space in the housing. This was the first

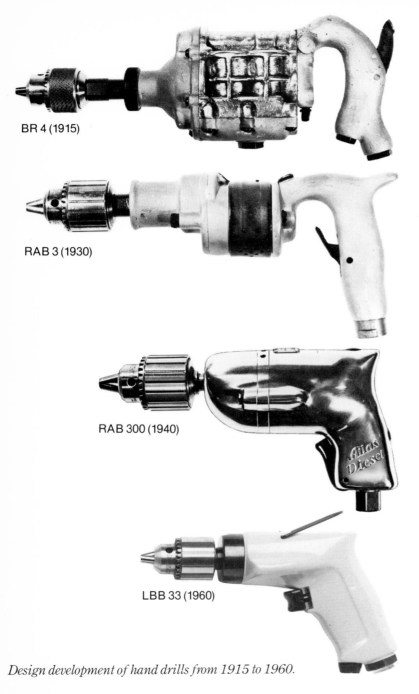

BR 4 (1915)

RAB 3 (1930)

RAB 300 (1940)

LBB 33 (1960)

Design development of hand drills from 1915 to 1960.

time the technical prerequisites existed for combining the motor housing and the handle, without the grip becoming far too large.

Consequently, when the RAB 300 appeared in 1940, it was equipped with a pistol grip.

We can also see a proper thumb grip support on the RAB 3. It's still there, but its size has been reduced on modern machines as a result of reduced overall weight.

One detail that is important to note is the angle of the handle in relation to the longitudinal axis of the tool.

The handle of the RAB 3 had been designed with an angle of 80° in relation to the longitudinal axis. The only reason for this must have been that in the 1920's when the machine was designed, the designers were already aware that one should avoid working with the wrist bent. A handle which is held in the hand must be angled in such a way that the wrist will remain straight.

Hands differ in size, so what suits one does not suit the other. The angle of grip, however, is roughly the same.

The choice of handle angle on the LBB 33, which was designed in the 1950's, was based on better knowledge than previously. However, it is interesting to note that ergonomic awareness existed long before.

In fact, the LBB 33 was also developed in co-operation with medical expertise.

The basic thought behind it was to combine a power grip, such as when gripping a hammer shaft, with a precision grip such as when gripping a pen.

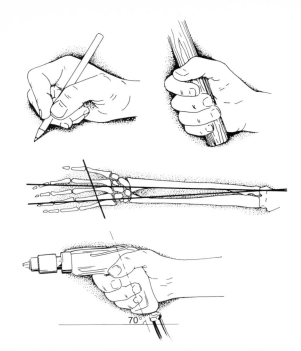

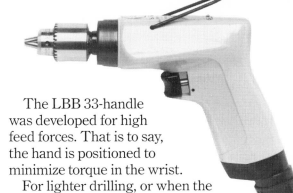

The LBB 33-handle was developed for high feed forces. That is to say, the hand is positioned to minimize torque in the wrist.

For lighter drilling, or when the handle is used on a screwdriver, a low position grip can be desirable. The new LBB 24 has been designed so that the operator can switch comfortably from a high to a low grip.

The pistol grip combines power and precision. The angle of the grip follows the arm anatomically.

Illustration of the end product (LBB33) and the different stages of design development by means of clay models.

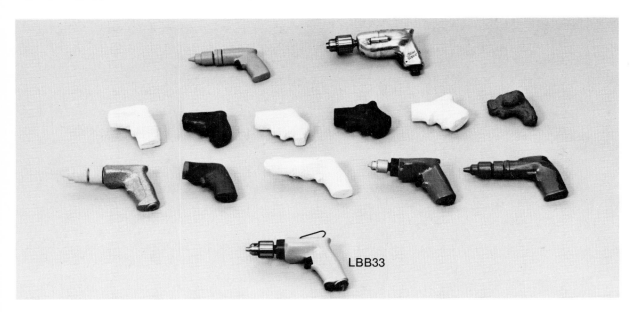

LBB33

19

In other words, this part of the handle has been made longer than on the LBB 33. A good rule when designing handles is that the operator should be given the possibility to shift grips while working, in order to redistribute the load among different groups of muscles and thus avoid localised exhaustion.

To summarize, the following applies:

A pistol handle with a high grip is chosen for large feed forces.

The right grip for the job.

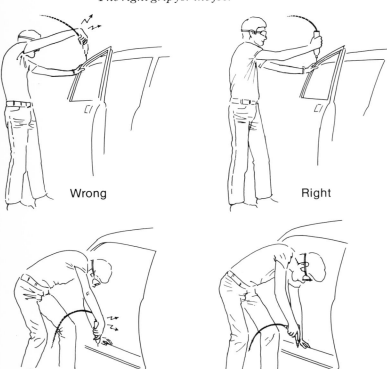

Wrong   Right

Wrong   Right

Rearranging the work piece for achieving the optimal working position.

A pistol handle with a low grip is chosen for low feed forces. A low grip also reduces the revolving torque that occurs in the wrist when driving screws in wood or other tough materials.

Straight handle

It is important that we try to design a workplace so that hands and arms can function as far as possible in a natural position.

Drills and screwdrivers
If a hole that is to be drilled or a screw that is to be tightened is situated so that is uncomfortable for the operator to use a pistol tool, then a straight tool is better.

Operator sitting with a straight tool
If high down feed force is required, in a sitting position the pistol grip is often used but the work must then be carried out with the elbow

raised, which may cause pain in the shoulder. In this case, probably the best solution is to rearrange the workpiece.

Throttle and support handles

Grinding is an operation that is carried out for long periods of time. Even if the necessary feed forces are relatively low, the work becomes tiring.

When our biggest grinder — the LSS 84 with a power output of 3.7 kW (5hp) — was introduced in the mid-1970's we found that its high power was not in demand, despite the fact that compressed air manufacturers had previously been competing with one another, increasing the power of their tools with every new design. But now it was impossible for the operator to fully exploit the power of the tool. Instead, this grinder came to be used mostly as a cutter.

When the new grinders LSS 56, 66 and 76 were designed, we limited their maximum output to 3.2 kW (4.3hp) to reduce weight.

A new feature when it comes to the handles on these tools is that they are adjustable. Different working positions may require different angles in order for the tool to feel as correct and comfortable as possible.

As the fingers of the hand have different lengths, it is ergonomically correct to allow the support grip to taper off towards the little finger so that all fingers can obtain an equally firm grip around the handle. Handles without sound attenuators in the ends must then be equipped with a bulge so that the hand does not

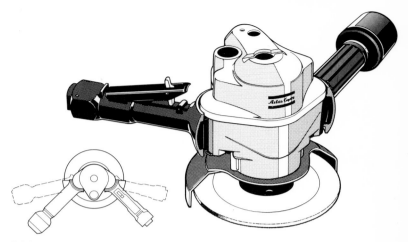

LSS66 Grinder. Multi-adjustable handles to suit different operators and applications.

slip off the grip. From a point of view of strength, the tapered grip is not important as it is mainly the thumb, index and middle fingers which maintain the strength of the grip.

Compared with the old machine the handles have been moved towards the front of the machine. This gives less torque in the wrists when grinding.

Handle dimensions for men and women

The optimal diameters for round handles are 38 mm (1.50') for men and 34 mm (1.34') for women. In order to meet technical demands for, among other things, available power, one is sometimes forced to increase these sizes. We do this very reluctantly, primarily because more women are entering industry and few tools are specifically designed for women. Another reason is that the size of a woman's hand is smaller, and her muscle strength is considerably lower.

Tendonitis

Inflammation of the tendons is a common complaint and can be a great handicap. The most famous symptom is tennis elbow or epicondylitis.

The muscles that enable us to stretch our hands and fingers are attached to the outer epicondyle of the upper arm bone, and if this attachment point is overloaded, inflammation may occur. The classical way of diagnosing this injury is to ask the injured person to slowly bend the wrist backwards (dorsal extension) and at the same time counteract the motion. The muscles attached to the outer epicondyle are then tightened and the inflamed area responds by causing pain.

Which common working situations can we find which impose this type of load? We have previously mentioned that the transmission of high feed forces imposes loads on the muscles which stabilize the wrist, including those that are attached to the outer epicondyle. Here, it would be reasonable to suppose that it is precisely these high feed forces that cause excess load on the tendon attachments. However, our experience of this type of problem is not associated with high feed forces, but rather with the absence of feed forces, i.e. when the hand tool is transferred from a standby position to a working position.

In other words, the tool mass creates force which results in torque in the wrist. To prevent the wrist from bending, we tighten the wrist muscles. The torque in the wrist can apply to both bending and twisting, depending on the design of the hand tool. In practically all cases, the above-mentioned muscles are engaged. The best remedy for this problem is to inform users that if possible, both hands should be used when hand-held machines are moved, or that the tools should be suspended by balancers.

The Carpal tunnel syndrome

A number of tendons in their sheaths, together with the median nerve, move in the carpal tunnel.

From a cross section of the right hand wrist through the outer line of wrist bones, we can see that the carpal tunnel can easily become congested.

The section shows the wrist in its initial functional position.

If the wrist is then forced to bend backwards, (hyper extension) the carpal tunnel is further contracted. The reduction in volume inside the carpal tunnel causes the median nerve to be compressed.

It has also been established that various types of grips exert the tendons in the tunnel in

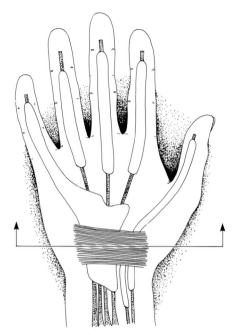

Position of the carpal tunnel

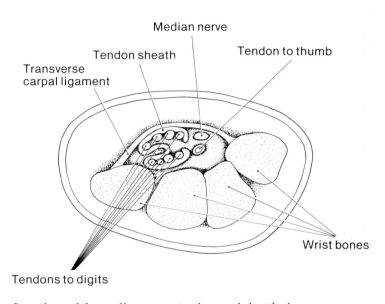

Locations of the median nerve, tendon, and sheaths in the carpal tunnel

different ways. A pinch grip gives a 20-50% higher load than a closed fist.

Furthermore, if the wrist is also twisted towards the thumb the median nerve may even become pinched.

A pinched median nerve can have the following consequences: pain, numbness, tingling, clumsiness and lack of sweating in the parts of the hand innervated by the median nerve. These symptoms often arise while the victim is resting in bed.

Some people experience these problems while others don't. It is highly likely that the working method plays a major role in the development of such an injury. One thing is certain, however. Women are more vulnerable than men. This can be because their carpal tunnels are narrower. As we have said, this may also be due to the fact that women's muscles are considerably weaker than men's, and when handling tools, perhaps women often take support from the skeleton when muscle power begins to fail them, i.e. that they allow the wrist to be completely bent especially during tool transfers between tasks.

We should try to work as close as possible to the body's natural anatomical stance.

Triggers and trigger forces

Various types of tools have different types of triggers.

The trigger often has some form of safety catch to prevent inadvertent starting. For product safety reasons this particularly applies to grinders. Most of them have a "dead man's grip", i.e. the tool stops the moment the trigger is released.

Finger trigger
Most pistol grips are equipped with finger triggers. These are primarily for index and/or

When activating a finger trigger, the middle part of the finger should be used, otherwise nodules can form and cause pain in the tendons.

middle finger usage. As a general rule the trigger should be activated by the middle phalanx and not the distal phalanx, as a nodule can develop in the flexor tendon on the inside of the finger. This nodule will not be able to move in the tendon sheath, resulting in pain. This condition is usually called "Trigger finger".

When working with drills with low as well as high grip, the index or middle fingers respectively are used to activate the trigger.

Often the trigger is designed so that it functions in two stages.

At start-up, only small forces are needed to start the tool. During this phase we look for the place where the hole is to be drilled. After the drill has started to bore, the trigger force is increased to approximately 10 N, at which point the pressure point is passed and the drill then operates at maximum power.

A certain number of tools require high precision with just a slight touch of the trigger. This is true, for example, of work with a riveting hammer. Here, the operator should be able to strike a few light blows to begin with, in order to partly alert the operator working on the opposite side of the workpiece that a new rivet is on its way, and partly to knock the new rivet in the riveting hole. During the riveting process, which lasts for little more than a second, the riveter must maintain full control over the operation. For the same size rivet, riveted in similar material the operator uses almost as many blows for each rivet. This is remarkable considering the tool strikes 30 blows per second, i.e. so fast that we do not

Riveting is a precision process that places high demands on the trigger function.

have time to count each blow but rely on our sense of hearing, touch and on experience to control the process.

The example shows a tool which is used intermittently. Tools which are used on a more continual basis place other demands on the trigger.

A spray painting gun, for example, is activated as often as every other second for long periods of time. Here it is important to have low

trigger forces so that the bending muscles on the inside of the forearm are not overexerted.

A high pressure gun such as the ECCO 300 required that a number of technical problems were solved in design, as the trigger force must be low at the same time as the pressure inside the gun to be overcome by the trigger, is extremely high.

Here, both the index and middle fingers are used to avoid exerting small muscle groups, as

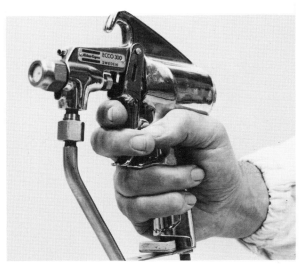

Two finger trigger for continuous, frequent work.

For repetitive, non-precision work four fingers can be used.

the trigger action is often carried out with short time intervals.

An additional reason for low trigger forces

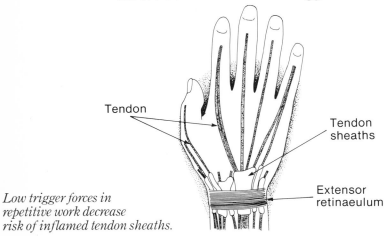

Tendon

Tendon
sheaths

Extensor
retinaeulum

*Low trigger forces in
repetitive work decrease
risk of inflamed tendon sheaths.*

with this type of repetitive work is the risk of tenosynovitis, which is inflammation in one of the tendon sheaths, normally on the back of the hand.

The symptom is pain, swelling, tenderness and a reddening of the hand, the wrist and/or the forearm.

Strip trigger

Here, four fingers co-operate to activate the trigger, which distributes the force and reduces the risk of exhausting the bending muscles. This trigger is used for products where the action occurs frequently. The stability of the grip is low, which is why it should only be used for products with low precision requirements and low weight.

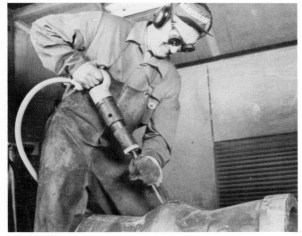

Thumb triggers for two entirely different work situations.

Thumb trigger

The most common type of thumb trigger is to be found on chipping hammers and other similar tools.

From an ergonomic point of view, this may appear to be a rather unusual location on a bow handle where feed forces are often high and, consequently, where the demand for a stabilized wrist is also high, and where the wrist is often bent backwards somewhat (dorsal extension). To then impose an extra load on the thumb with the trigger, resulting in pressure on the median nerve in the carpal tunnel, may appear to be asking for carpal tunnel syndrome. However, few cases of this have been reported which may indicate that the load on the thumb is not so extensive. The trigger force is an integral part of the feed force and the operator need not squeeze so hard.

At an early stage of design development, the trigger was positioned on the inside of the grip and one or more fingers were required to activate this function. This was thought to be less satisfactory, most likely as a result of increased load on the finger muscles.

An additional thumb trigger, is the button trigger for reversal, which may be positioned on the pistol grip or on a straight grip as on the straight LU 24 screwdriver.

The grip stabilizes the tool and the thumb controls the trigger.

Push trigger

A common trigger for screwdrivers is a push trigger which starts the tool the moment it is pressed down onto a screw. This increases speed as the entire hand is used to control the tool.

Lever trigger grinder with two-step function for low trigger forces and lengthy grinding sequences.

An old hand drill with a butterfly-type trigger.

Lever trigger

With grinding, where work can continue for long periods, the lever trigger is extremely common.

The trigger is activated by the hand closing around the trigger grip — the trigger force is then a part of the feed force.

Even if the operator presses the lever with the entire hand, the force must be kept low. This can be difficult to achieve at the precise moment of start, when full pressure loads the valve and gives high opening forces.

In our new range of grinders this problem has been solved with a two-step function. The valve functions so that the small area opens first to equalize the pressure to a certain degree, after which the main valve opens.

Twist trigger

Polishers or other tools which are used in processes with little risk of injury, can be equipped with twist triggers. In order not to affect the wrist with a twist torque these handles are often manufactured without spring-return function.

The advantage of this type of handle is that the operator can easily switch grips i.e. the operator is not required to hold the trigger down. This possibility relieves the muscles of the hand and forearm.

Butterfly trigger

This trigger is also frequently manufactured without a spring-return function. The trigger is mainly controlled with the thumb.

We have previously mounted this trigger on drills and grinders, as well as other tools, but have now abandoned it for safety reasons.

Torque reaction in handles

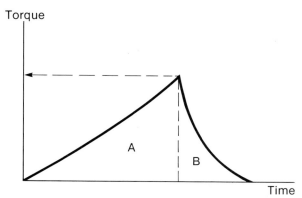

A fast-action clutch lowers the total impulse A + B and thus the recoil.

When we tighten a nut with a spanner, we apply a force on the handle which, multiplied by the length of the handle, gives the torque on the nut.

If we allow an angle nutrunner to do the same job, we have to hold back the handle with the same force, providing that the wrench and nutrunner are of the same length and that the torque rate on the nut is the same.

From a load point of view, this is the same thing. The difference is that the nutrunner attains the required force much faster.

In the case of the spanner, the operator controls the actual tightening process. In the case of the nutrunner, other factors control the process — for example, the rpm of the machine, torque rate of the joint etc.

For extremely soft joints there is no great difference, from a load point of view, between stall-type tools and tools equipped with clutches. If the torque in the joint is built up slowly we have enough time to react and the torque reaction in the hand is not such an unpleasant experience. However, the advantage of this tool, which is equipped with a clutch, is that it can achieve a pre-set torque with greater precision.

The harder the joint the more superior the clutch tool becomes from a load point of view; and the faster the disengaging function, the less torque reaction there will be in the hand.

This is illustrated by the above diagram:

Sector A depends on the speed of the tool, the desired torque, as well as the hardness of the joint. Sector B is a measurement of the speed of the clutchdisengagement.

The total sector A + B is a measurement of the impulse which strives to rotate the tool, i.e. to move the handle.

As a result, it is the responsibility of the tool manufacturer to minimize the total sector of A + B.

For a certain given torque level, A is dependent on the speed and power of the motor. The speed is limited for reasons of vane wear. The power of the motor can be increased, but only at the expense of weight and volume.

The LTV 46 nutrunner

Forces from balancers

If the force is created rapidly in the hand, we do not have time to engage an adequate number of motor units in the muscles, and the tool grip begins to move away from us. This is experienced as a torque reaction in the hand and is extremely unpleasant. A way of reducing this problem is to provide the machine with a fast clutch.

In our development work we have aimed at designing an extremely fast clutch. We have tried to avoid increasing the weight and volume of the tool because of other load factors.

LTV 46 can be run today on hard joints with a light hold on the handle using the thumb and index finger.

On a car assembly line, or at a single assembly work station, hand-held tools are often suspended by balancers.

There are several reasons for this. The balancer compensates for the weight of the tool, which reduces the load on the operator, and partly contributes to a well organized workplace in which the tools are always at hand.

In principle there are two types of balancers. The first type (RIL) has a lift force which continually increases the further the wire is extended. If a tool is suspended by this balancer, its weight is compensated for by the lift force. The balanced height can be adjusted by pre-setting the spring in the balancer. If it is desirable for the tool to be suspended at a higher level, the spring in the balancer block must be tightened.

The second type of balancer Colibri has a built-in wire drum which compensates for the change in the spring force depending on extension of the wire. If a tool is suspended by this balancer it can be positioned anywhere along the length of the extended wire. The spring force in the balancer block is pre-set according to the tool mass.

When choosing balancers, there are several contradictory requirements which should be fulfilled, which is why a certain knowledge of the technique is necessary.

The fundamental idea of the balancer is to compensate for the weight of the tool. At the same time, there is often a demand for the tool to be out of the way when not in use.

Springs in standard balancers can be tightened so that the balanced position for the tool is located above the point where it is to be used. In other words, when the tool has been used it is released, and the balancer lifts it away from the work zone.

The faster the tool is required to be lifted away, the greater the force that is imposed by the spring on the tool during use.

In order to achieve rapid lifting away of the tool, the wire can be equipped with a stop device which enables the balancer's springs to be highly tightened. The tool will then always hang suspended at the height dictated by the stop device.

Here, it is important to be aware of the fact that the compensation for tool weight, which is the main task for the balancer, can instead be exchanged for an upward force on the tool which is much greater than the weight of the tool. That is to say, the load on the operator has been increased instead of decreased.

Wrongly adjusted balancers or choice of settings, in large balancers, sometimes imposes a greater load on the operator than if no balancer was used at all and that the tool was simply placed in its rack at the workplace after use.

The second balancer, which compensates for

Tools suspended from balancers contribute to a well organized workplace and reduce load on the operator.

the spring constant, does not have the same disadvantageous upward force when pulling the tool down to the workpiece.

In certain work situations it may sometimes be necessary to carry out other tasks between operations with the tool. The tool can then often remain in the work zone. When the work has then been carried out, the tool can be pushed up and away from the work zone. The loads imposed on the hand-arm system from these balancers are small. The disadvantage with this balancer as opposed to the standard balancer can possibly be that the tools tend to remain at slightly different heights after use, if

the wire stop device is not used. If an operator forgets to push the tool up, it will remain suspended in the work zone. Varying heights can also mean that operators may bump into the tools as they move around the workplace.

However, there is every reason to believe that the Colibri balancer will be used to an ever increasing extent.

Another application for the Colibri balancer which has become increasingly widespread is to compensate for arm weight in highly repetitive assembly work carried out in a sitting position. This type of work is the prime cause of pain in shoulder and neck. By attaching the balancer to a sling in which the arm is allowed to rest, the arm can be made to feel weightless. This also reduces the load and thereby the symptoms often associated with this working posture.

It is important to point out that the introduction of balancers in this application necessitates previous consultation with trained specialists.

To avoid pain in shoulders and neck trough repetitive assembly work, arms can be allowed to rest in slings.

Handling risks

At the end of the 1960's the development of stall-type nutrunners was intensified, as the impact wrench was found to have two disadvantages. This was partly inaccurate tightening and partly high process noise.

The stall-type, hand-held tools which were developed were mainly angle nutrunners and pistol nutrunners. Both have a high degree of accuracy and low process noise.

Choosing stall-type tools must be made with greater knowledge of the technique involved than for impact wrenches. Angle nutrunners, for example, have a different shape than the impact wrenches they often replace, which can result in space problems at the workplace. The reaction bar on the pistol grip tool, which prevents torque reaction from being transmitted to the operator, must also be designed to suit the workplace.

In the beginning, it was discovered that operators were often injured by their hands becoming caught between the tool handle or reaction bar and the workpiece.

With angle nutrunners equipped with torque release clutches set for high torque levels, serious injury can be caused if the function should fail and the clutch should not release. In fact, this is a distinct possibility if the pressure in the main air supply should momentarily drop as a result of, for example, a sudden, large consumption of air in the vicinity. In this case, the air motor will not have enough power to release the clutch and the entire torque will react on the tool.

This problem has been solved in the LTV 46 with a pressure-sensing device which shuts off the tool the moment the pressure drops below a certain level. The danger inherent in these incidents was that they happened purely by chance and could therefore not be predicted by the operator.

What can be predicted as a potential risk, is if one holds a reaction bar on a pistol tool and the hand happens to come between the reaction bar and the workpiece. Pinching may result.

Serious injuries may occur particularly with tools such as the LTP 51, which is a high torque nutrunner with torque levels of up to 500 Nm (370 ft-lb).

This tool is interesting technically as it is equipped with two motors — one which quickly runs down the nut (stall-type nutrunners have previously been regarded as slower compared to impact wrenches) after which tightening takes place with considerably higher gearing.

At first glance this tool looks harmless enough, but in fact, it is a real power pack. We strive to make the operator aware of the potential risks involved with extensive information and product clarification.

Many factors influence our choice of tool type.

Impact wrenches give high torque; they are lightweight with low reaction torque, but produce a high process noise.

Stall-type tools are more accurate, quiet, sometimes difficult to position, and involve a risk of pinching.

The choice becomes largely a matter of the design of the entire workplace, and of the demands that are made on the working environment. A choice based on careful consideration often results in a well-functioning workplace with a high performance level and minimum risk of occupational injury.

Air line installation

One final subject that definitely influences the physical load on the worker is the compressed air line installation. An incorrectly dimensioned air line can give high pressure drops. This often means that power tools are selected over-dimensioned to cope with the technical demands, resulting in heavier tools than necessary. Stiff heavy hoses are also hindering.

Summary

An Ergonomicly designed power tool installed in a well-arranged workplace lays the foundation for high productivity and quality as well as low absenteeism.

It is important to train operators not to hold the reaction bar when tightening with a stall-type tool, due to the risk of pinching.

HOW TO DESIGN
noise controlled
power tools

HOW TO DESIGN
noise controlled power tools *by Lars Skogsberg*

HOW TO DESIGN
noise controlled power tools

Compressed air driven hand-tools are often used as examples of noisy machines. This is not surprising considering that air tools are extremely common and many old, compressed air tools are noisy. But we hope this chapter will demonstrate that with the aid of modern techniques it is possible to manufacture quiet, air-powered tools. So from now on, other culprits will have to serve as examples of disturbing noise sources in industry.

What is sound and how does it affect us?

Sound is pressure waves in the air

If you create pressure variation in the air via a reciprocating piston, and this pressure variation has a frequency of between 20-18000 cycles per second or Hz, we experience the pressure wave as a sound. The frequency range below 20 Hz is called infrasound and the range above 20 kHz is called ultrasound. The lowest pressure variation that can be detected by a person with normal hearing is approximately $2 \cdot 10^{-5}$ Pa, whereas the maximum pressure variation that can be detected with normal hearing without a person experiencing pain in approximately 20 Pa.

The loudest sound we are able to tolerate, is, therefore, one million times louder than the weakest sound we are able to detect. This considerable range makes it practical to use a logarithmic scale to express the sound pressure. The unit decibel (dB) can thus be quoted as:

$$L_p = 20 \cdot \log \left[\frac{p}{p_{ref}} \right]$$

where
L_p = sound pressure level (dB)
p = sound pressure
p_{ref} = reference pressure ($2 \cdot 10^{-5} Pa$)
($1\ Pa$ = $1\ N/m^2$ = 0,00001 bar)

This means that the audible range can be expressed in dB as the range 0—120 dB.

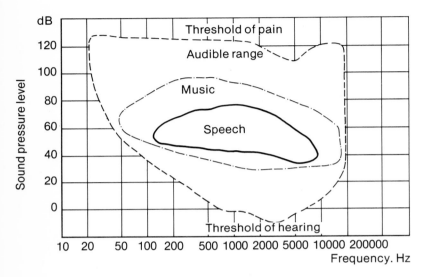

Fig. 1. The audible range can be compared with the frequencies and sound pressure levels that are typical for speech and music.

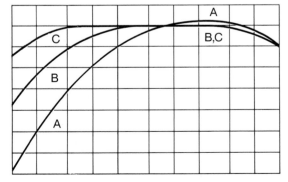

Fig. 2. Weighing curves for IEC standardized noise meters.

Pressure variations can have several causes. We usually refer to different sound sources. These can include, for example, vibrating surfaces, pulsating air flow or aerodynamic sound generated by escaping air. The propagation of sound and the method used to reduce it depend on the nature of the source. Further on in this chapter you will find examples from the field of compressed air techniques and of the methods employed by Atlas Copco to create low-noise tools.

The sound pressure level for the lowest sound that can be detected by the human ear varies with frequency (fig 1). In the same way, the sound pressure level varies for sounds of different frequencies which are experienced by the ear as being equally loud. If you design an electric filter with a dampening curve reciprocal to the sensitivity curve of the ear, and use the filter in a noise meter, the registered weighted value will be a measurement of how a sound is experienced. For many years there have been three such filters available (fig 2) which are called A, B, and C filters. These were intended to be used within different sound level ranges. The A-filter for low levels, the B-filter for the mid-range, and the C-filter for high sound levels. However, the only filter presently in use is the A-weighing filter which is used within the entire range and also to estimate other factors such as the risk of damage to hearing. In order to indicate that a value has been obtained via an A-filter, it is expressed as a dB(A) value.

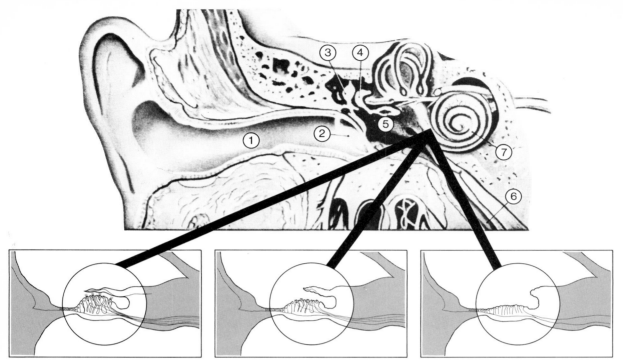

Fig. 3. The human ear. 1 The auditory canal 2 The eardrum 3—5 The ossicles 6 The eustachian tube 7 The cochlea. The basilar membrane divides the cochlea into two parts. On the membrane are hair cells. The three sketches show how the hair cells degenerate when exposed to loud noise.

How does noise affect human beings?

Noise is harmful
Extremely loud noise damages hearing. In rare cases, the damage is momentary and caused by shock waves from, for instance, an explosion. Damage to hearing normally occurs after many years of exposure to loud noise. Such damage is not sudden and total, but a gradual deterioration of the hearing which is most pronounced around the frequency of 4000 Hz. A hearing impairment of this type is determined by audiometric tests. The person to be tested listens to pure tones, one frequency at a time, in a set of headphones. The loudness of the sound is varied until the subject can just about hear the tone. The difference between the loudness of the sound and a reference sound level, represents the amount of hearing deterioration expressed in dB.

Sound, which reaches the eardrum via the auditory canal, is carried via the bones of the middle ear and oval window to the cochlea which is a fluidous organ, divided along almost its entire length by a membrane called the basilar membrane. The nerve cells (hair cells) from which we obtain our perception of sound are located on this membrane. Lengthy exposure to excessively high sound levels can damage these hair cells resulting in loss of hearing.

Impulse noises, i.e. noises that include short sound peaks, such as hammer blows, the noise of gunfire, or eccentric presses, are especially harmful. The protective mechanism in the ear does not have time to react. This mechanism dampens the movement of the bones of the middle ear. When activated, the sensitivity of the ear, particularly to lower frequencies, is reduced. The muscles are activated by the brain whenever a high sound level is experienced. The level required in order for the brain to activate the muscles is between 75 and 90 dB(A). The time it takes for these signals to reach the brain via the nerves and from there to the muscles is 0.3 — 0.5 seconds. It is impossible, therefore, for short sound peaks to be dampened by this protective mechanism. It is interesting to note, however, that high sound levels created by impulses are thought to be more harmful to hearing than continuous noise at the same level, even when the level is so high that the stapedius muscle is constantly activated. The reason for this phenomenon is not entirely clear.

High sound levels damage hearing under all circumstances, and with exposure to sound levels of more than 85 dB (A) for long periods, ear protectors must be used. The degree of protection required depends on the level of noise involved.

Noise is disturbing
High sound levels over long periods of time damage hearing. For this reason, major efforts are being made to reduce sound at workplaces to harmless levels.

Even so, there are several good reasons to continue to work also with lower noise levels. Noise also has a disturbing effect. This is more readily understood if we regard hearing from a historical perspective. As early as several hundred million years ago, when life on earth existed only in the sea, the inner ear existed and functioned in practically the same way as we know it does today. Ever since, well developed hearing has been a characteristic of most of the progressive species.

The reason for this is that hearing is a vital function in the defence mechanism of animals. And today, the same effect is clearly visible in man. Most of us are startled by a sudden noise. We "jump", and the body's defence mechanism goes into action, for example, in the form of increased adrenalin production. We all know that undesirable sound can be extremely irritating, even if the sound level is low.

The level at which sound can be termed "acceptable" depends on the environment. 85 dB(A) in premises for heavy industry, 65 dB(A) in offices, and 35 dB(A) in a bedroom at night are levels which are often quoted. Hand tools should preferably have such low sound levels that they do not contribute to an increase in the general level of sound in a workshop. Unfortunately this is not always possible to achieve.

An example of a tool where the sound level has been considerably reduced, despite the fact that its previous level was already well below the limit at which sound becomes harmful to hearing, is the LUM 11 screwdriver. This tool is often used in premises where the overall noise level is low and, furthermore, where many screwdrivers are often used in the same premises. The tool was modified, partly to reduce noise from the exhaust outlet, and partly to prevent the tool housing from transmitting vibration. As a result, the noise level was reduced by approximately 10 dB(A) to 58 dB(A) and the tool became extremely popular with operators. The LUM 11 has now been replaced by the LUM 14, which has the same low noise level but gives 15% higher torque.

Sound is also disturbing in that it prevents us from hearing other, perhaps more important sounds, such as warning signals. This concept is normally called "masking". Tests have shown that excessive masking occurs if the disturbance noise has the same frequency as the sound you want to be able to hear. Even if the frequencies don't coincide, masking can occur if the disturbance noise has a level exceeding that of the signal. Also, the signal is more easily disturbed if the centre frequency of the unwanted, disturbance noise is lower than that of the signal.

Sound measurement

Measuring sound — Why?
As mentioned earlier, the ear is a marvellous measuring instrument. The difference between the highest and the lowest audible sounds are greater than most measuring instruments are able to record. The ear can detect extremely slight deviations in frequency. Both ears together give us the possibility to determine where a sound is coming from. So why do we need electrical measuring instruments for noise?

The ear is good at experiencing changes in sound, but inadequate at determining absolute values for both frequency and amplitude.

Sound must be measured in order to verify hazards to hearing or the risk of disturbance. We need to measure in order to find out how much sound is emitted by a certain tool and at what frequencies, in order to give ourselves the possibility of changing the tool for the better. We differentiate between two methods of measuring sound. Health hazard measuring, or immission measuring aims to determine the level of sound to which the human ear is exposed in a particular environment. Machine noise measurement, or emission measurement, aims to determine the amount of noise emitted from a certain source.

Health hazard measurement
Even today it is not sufficiently well known which sounds are harmful to hearing, partly

41

because the dB(A) value is not always applicable, and partly due the fact that the "danger level" varies from person to person. There are standards, however, stipulating what levels are to be regarded as harmful. The permissible level for an 8-hour working day and the relation between the permissible level and the exposure time, varies from country to country.

Health hazards measured in dB(A)
When measuring the risk of damage to hearing, the sound level is measured in dB(A), where (A) means that the electrical signal during measuring is weighted with the A-filter mentioned earlier. The reasons for using the dB(A) value as an estimate for damage risk is

not very clear but the method is accepted all over the world.

The equivalent value and noise dose
For sound with a level that varies with time, a conventional noise level meter cannot be used to estimate the average value during the measuring time. Instead, an integrating sound level meter is used which registers an average sound energy value for a certain measuring period. This value is called the equivalent value, and is defined as follows:

$$L_{eq} = 10 \cdot \log \left[\frac{1}{T} \int_0^T \left(\frac{p_A(t)}{p_{ref}} \right)^2 dt \right]$$

where
L_{eq} = the equivalent value
T = total measuring time
$p_A(t)$ = the A-weighted momentary value
p_{ref} = the reference pressure (20 μPa)

We can say that the equivalent level is the level of continuous sound with the same energy as the varying sound which has been measured. In order to determine the risk of damage to hearing, a mean value is obtained of the equivalent values a worker is subjected to during a typical working period; with consideration given to the length of exposure for each part. The permissible size of this dose differs from country to country (fig.5).

The level termed "Halving level" in fig. 5 means the change in level which causes the highest permissible exposure time to be reduced by half. As the table shows, in different

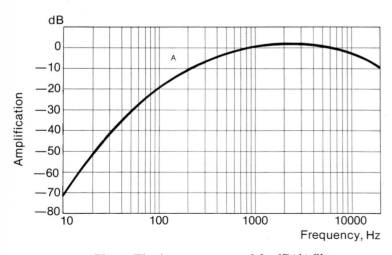

Fig. 4. The frequency curve of the dB(A) filter.

EEC member state	Steady noise level (dB(A))	Time exposure (h)	Halving level (dB(A))	Over-riding limit (dB(A))	Impulse peak SPL (dB)	Impulses (no./ day)
Germany	90	8	—	—	—	—
France	90	40	—	—	—	—
Belgium	90	40	—	—	—	—
Luxemb.	—					
Netherl.	—					
UK	90	8	3	135	150	—
Irish Rep.	90	—	—	—	—	—
Italy	90	8	5	115	140	—
Denmark	90	40	3	115	—	—
Others						
Sweden	85	40	3	115	—	—
Norway	—					
USA (Fed.)	90	8	5	115	140	100
Canada (Fed.)	90	8	5	115	140	—
Australia	90	8	3	115	—	—

Fig. 5. Table of national standards for exposure limits. In the column "Time exposure" 8 refers to 8 hours/day and 40 refers to 40 hours per week. (From B & K)

countries, either 3 or 5 dB corresponds to a halving of the time. 3 dB is the value recommended by ISO.

The total dose can be calculated if the duration and level of the various sounds to which the worker is exposed are known.

This is calculated with the aid of the following formula:

$$L_{eq} = 10 \cdot \log \left[\frac{1}{T} \sum t_i \cdot 10^{0,1 \cdot L_{p_i}} \right]$$

where
T = total time
t_i = the time for each part
L_{p_i} = the sound level for each part

The formula looks complicated but an assessment can be made without difficulty using a scientific calculator. A couple of examples can highlight the important rules of thumb when estimating the total dose.

1. During a 40-hour working week, the worker is exposed to 75 dB(A) for 35 hours and to 95 dB (A) for 5 hours.

$$L_{eq} = 10 \cdot \log \left[\frac{1}{40} \left(35 \cdot 10^{7,5} + 5 \cdot 10^{9,5} \right) \right]$$

$$L_{eq} = 86,3 \text{ dB } (A)$$

2. During a 40-hour working week, a worker is exposed to 95 dB(A) for 5 hours. For the rest of the time he is in what can be termed as a low noise environment.

$$L_{eq} = 10 \cdot \log \left[\frac{1}{40} \left(5 \cdot 10^{9,5} \right) \right]$$

$$L_{eq} = 86,0 \text{ dB } (A)$$

These two examples show that even short periods of loud noise completely dominate the total noise dose.

Machine noise measurement

The previous section dealt with methods and criteria for determining the amount of noise a worker is exposed to. This section will deal with the methods required for determining the amount of noise produced by a tool. The aim of these measurements is either to obtain a value of the total noise emitted by the tool, or to understand why a tool emits noise and therefore provide a basis for making noise-reducing modifications.

Sound intensity. Sound power

In order to discuss machine noise measurements, some additional definitions are required. Consider a loudspeaker membrane which moves backwards and forwards inside a tube. Pressure waves are emitted from the membrane and travel down through the tube. These waves develop at the speed of sound (340 m/s in air at room temperature). If the frequency of the membrane is between 20 Hz and 18 kHz, the pressure waves will be experienced as sound. In order to set the membrane in motion a certain amount of power needs to be applied. This means that the sound which is sent down through the tube is transporting energy. The amount of energy per unit area which is transported in this way is called Sound Intensity.

$$I = p \cdot u$$

where I = the sound intensity
   p = the sound pressure in the point
   u = the particle velocity perpendicular to the surface

In the tube, the sound pressure and the particle velocity are in phase, which means that the pressure and velocity are at maximum at the same time. The intensity can then be written as:

$$I = \frac{p^2}{\rho \cdot c}$$

where p = the sound pressure
   ρ = the density of the air
   c = the speed of sound

$\rho \cdot c$ in this case is a constant value which is called the acoustic impedance of the air.

The intensity can also be expressed as a logarithmic quantity:

$$L_I = 10 \cdot \log \left[\frac{I}{I_{ref}} \right]$$

where L_I = the sound intensity level (dB)
   I_{ref} = the reference intensity $(10^{-12} \ W/m^2)$

With this choice of reference quantity the sound intensity level will be equal to the sound pressure level at any point in a free field. In the tube the total sound power that is transported is:

$$W = I \cdot A$$

where W = the sound power
   I = the sound intensity
   A = the cross sectional area

In the same way as above, the sound power level will be:

$$L_W = 10 \cdot \log \left[\frac{W}{W_{ref}} \right]$$

where L_W = the sound power level
   W_{ref} = the reference power $(10^{-12} \ W)$

Free field and reverberation field
The previous section describes a simple connection between sound pressure and sound intensity. This is only applicable when pressure and particle velocity are in phase. This is extremely important and is the real reason for the building of more or less sophisticated sound measuring laboratories around the world.

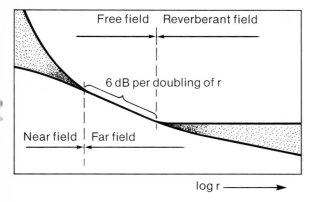

Fig. 6. *Variation in sound pressure with distance from a sound source in a room. Close to the source, the plane waves have not yet developed. At a distance far from the source, the sound is influenced by reflections from the walls.*

Fig. 6 shows how the sound pressure diminishes as the distance from the source increases. At close proximity to the source, the plane sound waves have not had time to develop, and pressure and particle velocity are not in phase. At a distance far from the source, reflections from other objects and walls add to the pressure measured by the microphone. In order to be able to measure the sound pressure at a number of points around a noise source and thereby calculate the projected sound power, measurements must be taken in a free field area where sound pressure and particle velocity are certain to be in phase and reflections do not make a significant contribution. These conditions exist in echo-free measuring chambers, where free field measurements are possible in large areas of the room.

In recent times, thanks to modern electronics, engineers have succeeded in producing intensity measuring instruments. These instruments measure with two microphones placed at a short but precisely determined distance from each other. The phase difference between them is measured in order to determine the sound intensity across an area at right angles to the axis between the microphones. This method makes it possible to perform measurements of radiated sound power from a machine without the use of sophisticated measuring chambers. This new technique is extremely promising and within a few years is expected to change a great many methods currently used to measure machinery noise.

Most machine measurement standards available today presuppose the use of echo-free measuring chambers, or require verification that the measuring operation has been carried out in a free field. This can be done by measuring the sound pressure difference between two points along a straight line through the source. If this is according to the

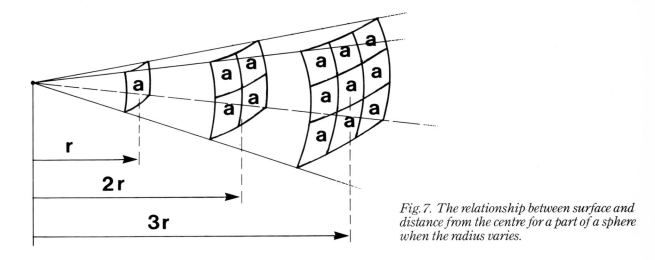

Fig. 7. *The relationship between surface and distance from the centre for a part of a sphere when the radius varies.*

law of distance below, it can be assumed that both points will lie within the free field area.

Law of distance
The sound pressure around a source depends on the distance from the source.

It decreases as the distance from the source to the measurement point increases. The difference in the sound pressure level between two measurement points is:

$$\Delta L_p = 20 \cdot \log \frac{r_1}{r_2}$$

where ΔL_p = the difference in noise level
r_1 = the distance from the noise source to measurement point 1
r_2 = the distance from the noise source to measurement point 2

Calculations according to the previous formula can be illustrated as follows: If $r_2 = 2r_1$ is inserted into the formula, we obtain:

$$\Delta L_p = 20 \cdot \log (1/2)$$
$$\Delta L_p = -6 \text{ dB}$$

This means that in a free field, the sound pressure level will drop by 6 dB if the distance is doubled.

Image sources and reflected sound
The effect of reflecting surfaces can be roughly estimated if the surface is regarded as being totally reflecting. It can then be assumed to give rise to a mirror source of sound. (Fig. 8). If the measuring point is situated between the wall and the source the following formula can be derived:

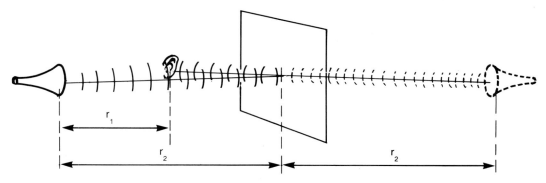

Fig. 8. The effect of reflection from a wall can be approximately calculated if the reflection is assumed to emanate from an image sound source behind the wall, and at the same distance from the wall as the actual source of sound.

$$L_{pr} = L_p - 20 \cdot \log \frac{2r_2 - r_1}{r_1}$$

where
L_{pr} = sound level from mirror source
L_p = sound level without reflecting surface
r_1 = distance from sound source for measurement point
r_2 = distance from sound source to reflecting surface

To arrive at the total sound level at a receiver point, the sound level from the image source can be added to the sound level from the direct sound.

Sound from several sources.
In many cases it can be of interest to calculate the sound level from several inter-connected sources. Direct-radiated sound amplified by reflections is one example. Several machines in operation at the same time in the same room is another.

An individual machine generates a given sound output to the surrounding area. At a given measurement point the intensity of this sound is I_1. Another machine at the same point gives rise to the intensity I_2. The total intensity at the point then becomes $I_1 + I_2$. Intensity is proportional to the square of the sound pressure. So, to add two intensities you must add the squares of the sound pressures. In the logarithmic terms used for sound this can be expressed:

$$L_{p tot} = 10 \cdot \log \sum 10^{(L_{pi}/10)}$$

where
$L_{p tot}$ = total sound pressure level at the point
L_{pi} = sound pressure level from source (i)

47

The formula can be easily applied directly by means of a scientific calculator.

A couple of examples are in order here.

1. Noise from two equal sound sources Lp are added together:

$$L_{p_{tot}} = 10 \cdot \log \left[10^{(L_p/10)} + 10^{(L_p/10)} \right]$$

$$L_{p_{tot}} = 10 \cdot \log \left[2 \cdot 10^{(L_p/10)} \right]$$

$$L_{p_{tot}} = 10 \cdot \log \left[10^{(L_p/10)} \right] + 10 \cdot \log 2$$

$$L_{p_{tot}} = L_p + 10 \log 2$$

$$L_{p_{tot}} = L_p + 3$$

Thus, the sound pressure level increases by 3 dB when two equal sound pressures are added together.

2. Noise from ten equal sound sources
Using the same reasoning we obtain:

$$L_{p_{tot}} = L_p + 10 \log 10$$

$$L_{p_{tot}} = L_p + 10$$

The sound pressure level increases by 10 dB.

3. Noise from one hundred equal sound sources:

$$L_{p_{tot}} = L_p + 10 \log 100$$

$$L_{p_{tot}} = L_p + 20$$

The sound pressure level increases by 20 dB.

Frequency analysis
In the chapter on measuring the risks of damage to hearing, the dB(A) weighting of a measured signal was described as a means of emulating the sensitivity of the human ear. In connection with the measurement of noise from machines, dB(A) is important because it provides a measure of how the sound from the machine is experienced by the user. However, to establish how a machine should be modified to comply with current noise criteria, a more detailed type of analysis is necessary whereby the frequency composition of the sound can be examined. This is called frequency analysis and several different methods can be applied. The one selected will depend on how detailed the information must be. The most general information is obtained by means of octave band analysis. This divides the frequency range between 20 Hz and 20 kHz in 10 octave bands. This division is such that the centre frequency for each band is twice that of the centre frequency for the preceding band.

To obtain a higher resolution, there are several possibilities. A one-third octave analysis divides each octave into three equal parts. See fig. 9.

It is also possible to use a 1/12 octave band which provides a highly detailed picture of the frequency composition of the sound.

The recent, rapid developments in computer technology, coupled with a new method of calculating termed Fast Fourier Transform (FFT), which was introduced as late as 1965, has made it possible to calculate a frequency

Centre frequency	Band limits	Centre frequency	(Band limits)
— 16	14— 18	— 1000	895— 1120
20	18— 22	1250	1120— 1410
25	22— 28	1600	1410— 1790
— 31,5	28— 36	— 2000	1790— 2240
40	36— 45	2500	2240— 2810
50	45— 56	3150	2810— 3550
— 63	56— 71	— 4000	3550— 4470
80	71— 90	5000	4470— 5610
100	90—112	6300	5610— 7100
— 125	112—141	— 8000	7100— 8950
160	141—179	10000	8950—11200
200	179—224	12500	11200—14100
— 250	224—281	—16000	14100—17900
315	281—355		
400	355—447		
— 500	447—561		
630	561—710		
800	710—895		

Fig. 9. Table indicating centre frequencies for 1/3 octave and octave bands, and band limits.

analysis by means of digital methods. Using an FFT analyzer, a given frequency range can be divided into a number of equally wide bands. Most modern analyzers work with 400 or 800 frequency bands. By using this type of analyzer you can obtain highly detailed information of the frequency content of a signal. In addition, a two channel FFT analyzer permits the comparison of two signals. These instruments are expensive but they open up totally new avenues for tracing sound sources by means of advanced analysis.

Pneurop Test Code
Most major manufacturers of air-powered hand tools apply a method specified in the PNEUROP CAGI TEST CODE for measuring the noise generated by their tools. This method is designed to permit measurement without the aid of sophisticated measuring equipment and an echo-free measuring chamber. A summary of the most important points in the section of the standards dealing with hand tools is given below.
— Measurement shall be performed with the centre of the machine 1 m above a reflecting floor.
— A place for measurement shall be chosen, so that the measured value is at least 6 dB greater in each octave band of interest than the sound pressure levels measured at more distant points in the same direction from the source as the microphone locations.
— Measurement shall be performed using five microphones. Four are to be positioned one metre from the surface of the machine in a plane one metre above the reflecting floor, and the fifth one metre directly above the machine.
— The machines shall be operated running free and loaded to maximum output. The device used for loading shall be so designed that the sound from the device is at least 10 dB lower than the machine sound in each octave band of interest.
— Both the dB(A) value and an octave analysis must be recorded during measurement.

The standard contains a number of illustrations depicting suitable arrangements for different types of machines.

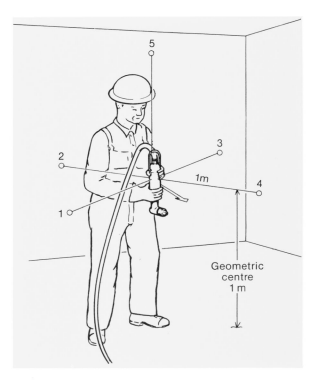

5

3

2

1m

4

1

Geometric
centre
1 m

Fig. 10. Example of an illustration from the PNEUROP TEST CODE showing recommended methods of measuring noise levels.

Atlas Copco Tools has been using this standard for many years, for performing measurements to be used as the basis for official standard sound data. For each speed variant for a given tool, at least five units are measured and the values obtained are a mean value of the sound emanating from the five tools. Measurement is conducted in a specially designed laboratory.

Atlas Copco Tools sound measurement laboratory
The sound lab was built as early as 1970 and consists of three chambers, one echo-free measuring chamber with reflecting floor, one control room and a room that serves as a combined storeroom and workshop. The echo-free room has brick walls and a concrete ceiling. The insides of the walls and ceiling are clad with a 0.5 metre thick, sound absorbent material arranged so that the density of the material rises the closer to the brick wall it comes. The inner dimensions of the room are 7x7x4.5 metres. The reflecting floor is a 25 cm thick concrete slab which is floating on an insulation carpet to prevent vibrations from the outside from propagating through the foundation to the measuring chamber inducing noise that could influence measurement.

The measuring chamber includes a supply of compressed air and electricity, along with water and drainage for cooling the brakes. A large exhaust air line leads from the room so that testing can be conducted on tools with exhaust air piped away. The measurement equipment in the room comprises a suspension device in which the five microphones are installed. The microphone cables are run into the control room. (See fig. 11).

In the control room, the signals are fed to five power supply units and continue from there to a channel selector. From there each signal, one at a time, is switched to a real time 1/3 octave band analyzer which is operated from a desktop computer. The computer controls measurement operations and stores and prints

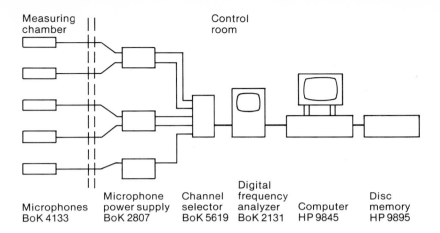

Measuring chamber

Control room

Microphones
BoK 4133

Microphone power supply
BoK 2807

Channel selector
BoK 5619

Digital frequency analyzer
BoK 2131

Computer
HP 9845

Disc memory
HP 9895

Fig. 11. The measurement system in the Atlas Copco Tools sound laboratory. The signals from five microphones are conducted via the microphone amplifier to the computer-controlled real time analyzer. The computer controls measurement and records the results.

out the results. With this type of system, other, higher precision measurements can also be made. These measurements can be used for the development of quieter machines.

Machine noise measurements for development purposes

Measuring prototypes places greater demands on repeatability than measuring machines, as it is important to be able to establish minor differences in sound from a certain prototype, before and after design modifications have been made. This type of measurement usually requires analysis of spectra with great resolution. For this reason we have the capacity to perform one-twelfth octave band analysis with our real time analyzer, plus access to a modern two-channel FFT type analyzer (Fast Fourier Transform). This equipment enables us to study a sound source in great detail and effectively analyze the result of a modification.

Difference between machine noise and health hazard measurement

Health hazard measurement and machine data measurement is dealt with in two separate sections of this chapter. As these two types of measurement are entirely different it is also important that they are not mixed together. Health hazard measurement is based exclusively on the prevailing working situation, while machine data measurement, on the other hand, describes machine noise under carefully specified operating conditions. Estimating the degree of noise to which a particular user will be subjected, based on known machine data is therefore extremely unreliable.

Certain facts must be obtained, such as the amount of time the tool is in use per day or week, the distance from the worker's ear to the machine, the presence of other sound in the room, possible amplification of the sound owing to reflection from objects in the vicinity of the machine, the directional characteristics of the machine and so on. The list could be longer. The crucial difference, however, is that the sound generated by the process, such as a grinding wheel working against a surface, is not included in the machine data published according to CAGI PNEUROP TEST CODE.

Machines for which a high process noise can be expected include all types of percussive tools such as riveting hammers, chipping hammers, impact wrenches as well as grinding machines. It is impossible to calculate the degree of noise to which the user will be subjected based on the machine data available for these machines. Still, dampening the noise emanating from these machines is far from futile.

A machine that generates low noise causes less disturbance when idling; it doesn't add to the overall noise level where the process noise is low and it is perceived as being less disturbing.

Sound reduction

Sound sources in pneumatic tools

Earlier sections have mentioned various sources of noise, such as vibrating surfaces, flow sound, and so forth. In the case of hand tools,

the different sources are broken down in a special way. There are primarily three types of noise that dominate the workplace:

1. Process sound — produced by contact between the machine and a surface. It radiates from the workpiece and sometimes also from the work bench.

2. Exhaust air sound — partly caused by the flow variation as the compressed air passes the motor, and partly by the aerodynamic sound generated in the exhaust air channel.

3. Vibration-radiated sound — from the surface of the machine produced by the moving parts of the machine and the flow of air inside the machine.

There is good reason to take a closer look at these three types.

Process sound
A vibrating surface radiates noise. The vibrations in our case are caused by a hand tool working against a given surface. The tool can be a chipping hammer, an impact wrench or a grinder. In each case it is the process itself that gives rise to the noise, and attempts to dampen it will generally impede the efficiency of the process. The amount of noise generated by a machine depends largely on the design of the workpiece.

As tool manufacturers, it is impossible for us to influence the design of the workpiece. In some cases it may be possible to change the method of working in order to lower the noise level. One of the most common means of doing this is by switching from impact type processes to other kinds. For instance, impact wrenches can be replaced by stall-type nutrunners. Stall-type machines are often integrated to form multiple nutrunners.

As mentioned earlier, some forms of process noise can be reduced by designing the tool to eliminate unnecessarily high frequencies in the blow. A frequency analysis of the blow indicates that it is made up of an exceptionally broad frequency spectrum. Hard surfaces that strike each other raise the high frequency part of the spectrum. High frequency components are effectively radiated from the surface of the workpiece. High frequency components created by the blow excite all the natural frequencies of the workpiece (in the same way as striking a church bell). The structure oscillates radiating noise. A thorough analysis of the work process reveals that the high frequencies of the impact are not always necessary. If they can be eliminated, then the noise from the workpiece can be reduced.

A good example of this can be found in the shipbuilding industry. Heavy hammers are used for moving massive piles into position before welding. An analysis of the process showed that the high frequency portion of the blow, generated right at the instant of contact, did not contribute to driving the pile. By covering the hammers with rubber it was possible to do the same job with much less noise. But it is easy to imagine the results if the same hammer was used for riveting. In other words, the high frequency portion of the impact is needed for some processes.

Exhaust air sound
Most noise produced by a pneumatic hand tool emanates from the exhaust air. There are two mechanisms which contribute to exhaust air noise. The variations in air flow through the motor and the sound generated aerodynamically in the exhaust channels.

Sound from a pulsating air flow
Each time one of the vanes in the vane motor passes an exhaust port, the air content contained between that vane and the next is emptied into the exhaust system. This occurs at a rate called vane frequency (revolutions per second times the number of vanes). The sound pressure caused by the pulsating exhaust flow at a distance from the exhaust opening is proportional to the rate of change of the flow.

$$p = \frac{I}{4\pi r} \cdot \frac{dQ}{dt}$$

where $\frac{dQ}{dt}$ is the rate of change

This means that the change of flow rate must be kept as small as possible without causing excessive back pressure.

Aerodynamic sound generated by an air flow
Aerodynamic sound is produced by air passing through a hole or opening at high speed. A good example of this is a blow gun. Other

sources of this form of noise are, for example, the outlet through sinter bronze exhaust or hole matrices. A frequency analysis of the noise reveals that the noise level rises with the increase in frequency to a maximum value at the frequency:

$$f = S \cdot u/d$$

where S = Strouhal's factor
(0.15−0.20 for air)
d = diameter of the hole
u = speed of air

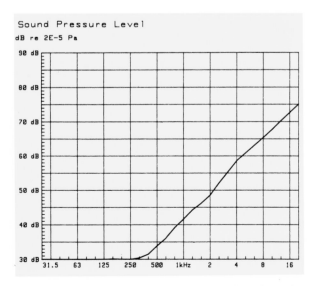

Sound Pressure Level
dB re 2E−5 Pa

Fig. 12. Frequency analysis from air flowing through a 2 mm hole in a container wall. The pressure accelerates the air up to but not above the speed of sound.

The overall sound output from a hole can be approximately expressed by the equation:

$$L_w = 80 \cdot \log (u) + 20 \cdot \log (d) - 52$$

where L_w = sound power level
u = speed of air
d = the hole diameter

From the above two relationships certain conclusions can be drawn.
— The noise level drops quickly as the exhaust velocity decreases
— Numerous smaller holes are better than one large hole in terms of noise generation, since their maximum level is achieved at a higher frequency. Thus the sound is easier to dampen using sound-absorbing material. A sinter bronze exhaust is in effect a hole matrix with many tiny holes.

A blow gun or a machine exhaust can also generate noise when the stream of air strikes an object. For this reason, and also because the high exhaust velocity tends to swirl dust to a greater degree, there is every reason to adapt the dimension of the air exhaust for low velocity.

Vibration induced sound
A vibrating surface can be compared to the piston in a pipe that was used earlier as an example of a source of noise. The machine casing of a hand tool is a source of noise although the levels are usually not large compared with, for instance, exhaust air noise.

As noise reduction devices grow more advanced, vibration-radiated noise is coming more into focus as a noise source on hand tools. The vibrations in a surface give rise to noise that depends on the vibration frequency.

In simple terms, the higher the frequency the greater the noise generated up to a given frequency, the critical frequency or the coincidence frequency. Above this, noise radiation remains constant regardless of the frequency. For hand tools this means that exhaust air noise is usually the chief cause of noise for frequencies around the vane frequency, while vibration-generated noise often dominate the frequencies above 5 kHz.

Methods for reducing noise from pneumatic tools

Reduction of process noise
It is possible to reduce process noise by designing the tool to eliminate unnecessary high frequencies in the impact.

For the removal of slag, the conventional scaler can be replaced by a machine like the RVM 06, which has a reciprocating chipping action.

The chisel is an integral part of the working piston and follows the reciprocating action of the piston. Thus, the machine is not an impact machine in the true sense of the word. It operates in a manner generating less high frequency vibration in the work surface. This means that the RVM 06 is able to remove slag at a lower noise level than was previously

Fig. 13. Ergo Pulse hydraulic-pneumatic nutrunners are examples of tools where process noise has been reduced by adopting new techniques.

possible. This is one example of how it is possible to lower process noise when working with hand tools.

In an impact wrench, a heavy rotating hammer strikes an anvil which, in turn, transfers the rotation energy of the hammer to the bolt. Here too, it has been proven that high frequency portions of the blow contribute only marginally to the work process. By transferring the energy in the rotating hammer to the bolt via a hydraulic impulse mechanism, the high frequency noise from the blow has been reduced. The result is that the overall noise has been reduced without noticeably affecting the operation efficiency of the machine. In addition, it is also easier to incorporate accurate torque control into the design of a hydraulic mechanism.

Piped-away air
The simplest and most effective means of reducing the noise generated by exhaust air is to use a hose to pipe it away. This also removes the oil fog that is carried in the exhaust air. The major drawback is that the machine must be fitted with an extra hose that must be considerably larger than the inlet hose, since it will be conducting expanded air. This makes the machine more cumbersome to handle.

Machines using dust extraction equipment are fitted with a large dust extraction hose. An additional hose is therefore only a marginal problem, so some of these machines incorporate an exhaust hose.

Sound-absorbing hoses
For machines with dust extraction equipment but without piped-away air, a sound-absorbing hose (patent pending) can be used. This is a plastic hose which is clad on the inside with a sleeve containing a sound absorbent material. A diffusor sits in the end of the hose for distributing the air over a large area which, in turn, lowers discharge velocity. This hose can sometimes also be used as an accessory for a separate air motor.

Tuned silencers
In some cases where size permits, tuned silencers can be used, consisting of a volume and an exhaust pipe of given length. For this type of silencer to be effective the length of both the volume and exhaust pipe is determined by the particular wave lengths of the noise, that is to be dampened.

The pipe and volume form an oscillating system. When the length of the chamber is a quarter of the wavelength of the added frequency, the oscillations in the chamber will be out of phase with the incoming oscillations, resulting in a sound reduction. The greater the diametric ratio between the pipe and the chamber, the more effective the dampening effect. A high air speed at constant flow through the silencer impairs efficiency.

The length of the silencer is determined by the wavelength of the sound to be dampened, which is why this type of silencer is not used very often for hand tools.

Silencers with volume and pressure drop
Silencer volumes with small dimensions in relation to wavelength can serve to reduce noise, together with a certain back pressure in the channel downstream of the volume. Sound reduction for this type of silencer can be expressed as:

$$D = 10 \cdot \log \left[1 + (\omega/\omega_f)^2 \right]$$

$$\omega = 2 \cdot \pi \cdot f$$
$$f = \text{frequency of sound}$$
$$\omega_f = 1/(R \cdot C)$$

where C = capacitance of volume
R = resistance of the exhaust air throttling

ω_f can also be expressed as:

$$\omega_f = 1.4 \cdot 10^5 \cdot q_v \, 1/(\Delta p \cdot V)$$

where q_v = the volume flow (m³/s)
Δp = pressure drop over the exhaust (N/m²)
V = volume of the silencer (m³)

Attenuation D can be expressed as:

$$D = 10 \cdot \log \left[1 + \left(\frac{\omega \cdot \Delta p \cdot V}{1.4 \cdot 10^5 \cdot q_v} \right)^2 \right]$$

If these equations are applied in an example, certain rules of thumb can be determined.

Consider two silencers with volume V and 2V respectively and simplify the expression for attenuation by writing

$$\frac{\omega \cdot \Delta p}{1.4 \cdot 10^5 \cdot q_v} = K$$

The difference in attenuation $D_2 - D_1$ gives:

$$D_2 - D_1 = 10 \cdot \log \left[\frac{1 + (2KV)^2}{1 + (KV)^2} \right]$$

Large values for K give:

$$D_2 - D_1 = 10 \cdot \log \left(2^2 \right) = 20 \cdot \log (2) = 6$$

The above computation demonstrates that
— doubling the volume of the silencer increases attenuation by 6 dB.

The same calculation can be used for a change in pressure drop or airflow and the following is arrived at:
— If the air flow through the silencer is doubled without increased pressure drop, attenuation will decrease by 6 dB
— If the back pressure of the silencer is doubled, attenuation increases by 6 dB

This is the most common method used for

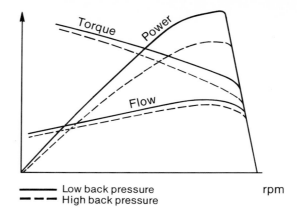

Low back pressure
High back pressure

rpm

Fig. 14. Characteristics of a governed air motor. Two curves are given for torque, air consumption and power as a function of motor speed. The two curves demonstrate how back pressure affects motor characteristics. Note that power is much more affected than torque and air consumption.

silencing hand tools since this type of silencer will not increase the size of the tool. However, the problem is that back pressure must be used which impairs the performance of the machine somewhat. For this reason it might be in order to take a closer look at how a rise in back pressure affects the performance.

Air consumption is only affected by the pressure on the inlet side of the motor and almost independent of back pressure. Torque is affected a great deal at high speed when air consumption and thus back pressure are large; whereas at low speed, the torque remains almost constant because air consumption is low. Output power is proportional to torque times rotational speed, and therefore highly affected at high speeds.

What does this mean for the user?
— A governed machine designed for an acceptable pressure drop at max. load has a

very low back pressure when running free and thus ineffective sound reduction.

— Increasing back pressure lowers the maximum output power without affecting air consumption. Thus specific air consumption increases.

—A machine with high back pressure can deliver the right idling speed and a good stall torque, and yet still lose much of its maximum output.

Active valve in the exhaust
Atlas Copco has solved the problem of achieving good sound reduction when the machine is running free, without causing excessive back pressure at maximum load by using a spring-loaded valve in the exhaust on governed machines. The spring is designed so that the back pressure in the motor exhaust remains about constant and is virtually unaffected by air flow. This results in effective

sound reduction both when running free and at maximum load. This type of silencer is available today for most governed grinders, such as the LSV 16, 26 and 36 angle grinders and the LSS 56, 66 and 76 vertical grinders.

Fig. 15 depicts the sound reducing system used in the LSS 56. A spring-loaded piston is located inside the support handle. When air escapes through the handle, the piston moves and thereby opens a number of radial holes. This system gives an almost constant back pressure inside the machine independent of air consumption. The aerodynamic noise generated when the air passes the radial holes is attenuated by means of the diffusor at the end of the handle. The hole matrix in the diffusor is designed to generate a very small pressure drop, and so the air speed in the outlet holes is low. Moreover, the diffusor can be twisted on the handle to enable the user to aim the escaping air in the most suitable direction.

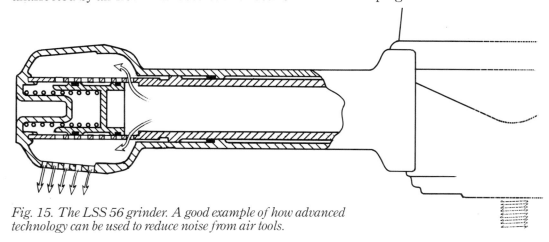

Fig. 15. The LSS 56 grinder. A good example of how advanced technology can be used to reduce noise from air tools.

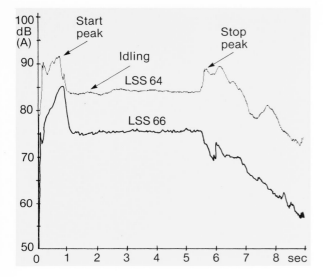

Fig. 16. Variations in dB(A) values for LSS 64 and 66 during start, idling and stop cycles.

This solution offers further advantages. The valve is closed when the machine stops and also when it is not in use. This protects the machine from contaminants which otherwise could easily find their way into the machine through the exhaust.

The noise generated in connection with start and stop, which for conventional machines is characterized by very pronounced peaks, is considerably lower for machines with active valves.

Fig. 16 depicts the difference between a conventional machine and a machine with an active valve through the start, idling and stop sequences. As is apparent, stop noise has disappeared entirely.

Reducing vibration-induced noise

As methods for reducing noise caused by exhaust air improve, the chief source of noise is increasingly becoming the vibration-radiated noise from the machine casing. In conjunction with development work on the LUM 11 SS, the problem of vibration-radiated noise was studied.

Fig. 17 shows a cross-section of a LUM 14. The rear and the coupling section of the

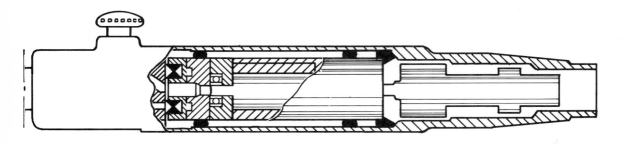

Fig. 17. The LUM 14 screwdriver. A tool designed to reduce noise emitted from the tool housing.

machine are screwed into an outer housing made of anodized aluminium. An inner housing containing the air motor and gears is carried on axial and radial rubber elements.

The predecessor to the LUM 14 was basically the same machine but without the double motor housing. Measurements of this machine with piped-away exhaust air revealed that the housing radiated noise of about the same magnitude as the exhaust air noise. Attempts were then made to limit the vibrations that were propagated to the housing.

Investigations showed that these vibrations stemmed from not one but several sources, such as the movements of the vanes in the cylinder along with the noise generated by the flow of air. Instead of conducting extensive development work to produce a motor with lower high-frequency vibrations, it was decided to isolate the outer shell from the motor using rubber elements. The motor rests basically on the axially positioned elements, but the radial O-rings prevent direct metallic contact between the casing and the motor. This form of vibration-insulation is designed solely for high frequencies and should not be confused with vibration-insulation done to lower the risk of vibration-related injuries to the hand, which is unnecessary for a screwdriver.

— The most realistic method of neutralising vibration-radiated noise emanating from the machine housing, is thus to isolate the air motor from the housing by means of rubber elements.

LSS 56, 66, and 76 — a new series of silent grinders

The new LSS machines are good examples of how the methods described earlier for reducing noise from a hand tool can be used in product development. It was an ambitious project. According to the requirements, the noise generated by the machines at peak load was not to exceed 90 dB(A), even for the largest machine. A table with the comparative values of the new LSS machines and the older machines, prove how well we have succeeded.

The LSS 53, predecessor to the LSS 56, was the first machine to be fitted with a handle incorporating an active valve. The new machine has the same low noise level but, in addition, delivers up to 30% higher output power at the same speed.

The LSS 76 has been restricted to 3.2 kW. Experiences gained from the LSS 84 have shown there is no demand for making use of the higher output.

LSS 56
This is the smallest machine in the range and due to low air consumption it is possible to use a support handle with integrated valve. The advantage of this is that it permits a greater volume between the motor and valve, thus enabling more effective sound reduction.

As is obvious from fig. 19, the machine has been permitted to broaden between the handles, where the greater volume does not affect the work.

The size of the handles allows the valve to

New tool					Previous tool				
Tool	Idling speed rpm	Max power kW	Running free	Max power dB(A)	Tool	Idling speed rpm	Max power kW	Running free	Max power dB(A)
LSS 56	6000	1.55	76	81	LSS 53	6000	1.15	74	83
	7200	1.65	77	82		7200	1.25	76	83
	8500	1.70	79	85		8500	1.46	78	84
LSS 66	6000	2.45	77	80	LSS 64	6000	2.40	82	92
	8500	2.60	81	86		8500	2.85	86	93
LSS 76	6000	3.2	76	83	LSS 84	6000	4.0	87	96

Fig. 18. Table showing major parameters for the new series of surface grinders compared to their predecessors. Note that LSS 53 was the first machine with an active valve in the support handle, which explains the low noise level for this machine.

produce a back pressure of 0.8 bar for the fastest model and 0.7 bar for the slowest. Both these values were measured at maximum load.

The radial holes in the middle pipe that are opened by the valve generate an aerodynamic sound. To reduce this, and also to achieve a reasonably low air outlet speed, the end of the handle has been fitted with a diffusor. The size of the outlet in the diffusor has been chosen to reach low outlet speed in combination with good noise reduction. The vibration-radiated noise from the machine housing has been dramatically reduced by suspending the motor between two rubber elements.

Fig. 19. The new LSS 56 grinder compared with its predecessor, the LSS 53. The new design shows how all critical dimensions are small while non-critical dimensions were allowed to grow.

Fig. 20 shows a dimensional comparison between the LSS 66 and the previous model, the LSS 64.

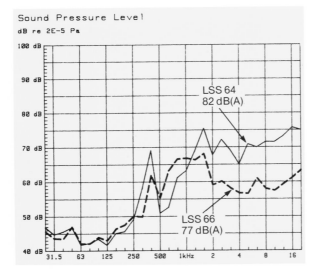

Fig. 21. 1/3 octave band analysis showing the difference between new and old design surface grinders.

LSS 66 and 76

Both of the larger machines have also been equipped with an active valve for outlet air. A rough estimate revealed that the air flow involved (50 l/s) was too great to permit the use of a valve in the handle. Instead, the valve was placed in the machine between the handles, where the increase in size is irrelevant.

Fig. 20 shows a dimensional comparison between the LSS 66 and the previous model, the LSS 64. The valve is located in the housing between the handles.

The drawback with this design is less volume in front of the valve. The advantage is that it permits optimum valve operation through a relatively large amount of space. Although the handle wasn't needed for the valve, it was decided that placing the air outlet in the support handle would give major advantages. It is easy to achieve a large hole area and thereby low outlet air speeds and it gives the operator the possibility to direct the flow of air in the most suitable direction. Designing the handle to permit a substantial air flow without generating excessive noise was not without problems. The various aerodynamic noise levels generated by the different handle designs were measured in a testing device which fed air through the handles. The design which was ultimately chosen produces a noise level of 82 dB(A) at a flow rate equivalent to that of the largest machine run at maximum power. This is low enough not to add to the overall noise level of the machine.

Fig. 21 shows a 1/3 octave band analysis of the noise from the LSS 66 and its predecessor the LSS 64 when running free. The vane frequency at 400 Hz is effectively attenuated in the LSS 66 by the active valve. In the LSS 64, the frequency range above 2000 Hz dominates in terms of vibrationradiated noise from the machine housing, while in the LSS 66 the dominant noise is generated by the outlet air flow.

These new machines are also equipped with motors mounted between rubber elements which reduce the vibration-radiated noise from the housing compared to the earlier models.

Termination of power tool noise dominance

As mentioned previously, the older compressed air driven machines were noisy. With modern technology, noise is no longer a negative factor nor a problem when it comes to choosing between air driven tools or tools driven by other methods. Now it is time to reduce other alternative disturbing noise sources in industrial workshops.

HOW TO DESIGN
vibration-controlled
power tools

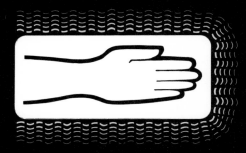

HOW TO DESIGN
vibration controlled power tools *by Bo Lindqvist*

HOW TO DESIGN
vibration controlled power tools

What are vibrations and how do they arise?

All hand-held machines transmit vibrations to our hands while we are working with them. Vibrations consist of a reciprocal motion in the handles which arises when a number of forces with varying directions and magnitude influence the machine and set it in motion. These forces consist largely of reaction forces from the work process. In other words, they arise while we are actually performing the task for which the machine is designed.

Vibrations in the handles may also be due to different forms of natural oscillations which are initiated by the process forces and imbalance in rotating parts. Movements of the handles may also be influenced by movements in the mate-rial being worked; movements which, in turn, are controlled by the process forces.

What we are concerned with, in point of fact, are fundamentally well-known mechanical phenomena; but it has nevertheless been found that vibration-damping measures usually mean completely new designs, which call for allocation of large resources that are also highly time-consuming.

How do they influence people?

Work with intensely vibrating machines for a long period of time may give rise to different types of injury. Main types of injuries likely to occur are largely vascular injury, nerve injury,

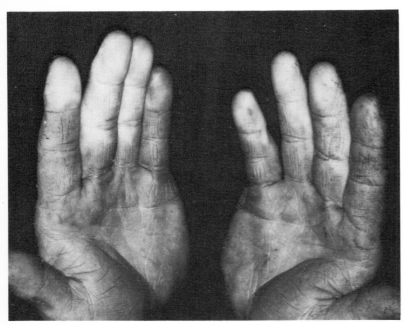

Vibration-induced white fingers during an attack.

skeletal injury and joint injuries. The mechanism between intensive vibration and the resulting injury has not yet been fully understood.

Vascular injury

With vascular injury, the walls of the vessels in the peripheral arteries, particularly in the fingers, have been thickened and, in consequence, the passage available for the blood has decreased.

The hands serve as the radiators of the body. In other words, if the body wishes to cool away heat, a large flow of blood through the hands is permitted, whereas if we feel cold the blood flow is reduced to a minimum. The ratio between the maximum and minimum blood flow is of the order of 200 times.

If the body wishes to reduce the blood flow by constricting the vessels (which is accomplished via the central nervous system), a damaged vessel which already has a narrower passage can become completely blocked up. No blood is able to get through and consequently the vessels and skin turn pale. This phenomenon has given this particular vascular injury the name white fingers or Raynaud's phenomena, VWF (vibration induced white fingers), TVD (traumatic vasospastic disease) etc.

The time for constriction is very short indeed, and, as a rule, the muscular activity in the smooth musculature of the vessels fades by reflex action, (dilatation). This is in order to protect the tissues against a shortage of oxygen and nutrition. When muscular activity decreases in a damaged vessel without any blood flow, the blood pressure is incapable of immediately increasing the dimension of the vessel. The sufferer then gets an attack of white fingers, revealed in a loss of feeling and in numbness and tingling on account of the shortage of nourishment and oxygen for the nerve cells. After a while, the fingers may turn blue (cyanosis), the reason being that the tiny amount of blood that succeeds in passing the vessels transfers all its oxygen to the tissues. The duration of the attack can be reduced by rubbing the hands, thereby activating the muscles and supplying heat. The attacks are triggered by general cooling of the body and not by the fact that we are working with a vibrating machine.

Nerve injuries
The fact that nerves can also be influenced by vibrations is demonstrated by, among other things, a decline in the ability to interpret through feeling two adjacent pressure points acting on the skin of the finger as two and not as one. This can be tested by making the finger run along two non-parallel rules and attempting to decide when the sensory impressions from the two rules coincide into one (or vice versa).

If we measure the sensory threshold for a vibration, and then hold on to a vibrating object for a short time and once again measure the sensory threshold, we will find that this threshold has been raised more for fingers injured by vibration than for uninjured fingers.

The consequence of an injury of this nature may be disturbed night sleep. The sufferer wakes because of a sensation that his arms have gone to sleep and he cannot move them.

Skeletal and joint injuries
High vibration amplitudes (at low frequencies) in combination with high feed forces cause wear on the surfaces of joints. Impacts can cause microfractures in skeletal bones and thus interfere with the supply of nutrition to joints. The injuries can give rise to pain in joints.

How do we measure vibrations?

It has been found that measurement of vibrations on hand-held tools is far more difficult than we originally envisaged. At the present state of the art, we are capable of measuring with high repeatability in the laboratory, but we are still somewhat apprehensive about making field measurements.

When measuring vibrations, it is very difficult to decide subjectively whether or not the results of our measurements are reasonable. We cannot simply touch an object and with any higher degree of precision determine the vibration frequencies and amplitudes. In other words, we must rely entirely on our electronics.

Measuring parameters
A motion can be described in terms of displacement, velocity or acceleration. Between these three units there are unambiguous relationships via integration and differentiation respectively. For the engineer, the most obvious unit is the displacement, which defines where the object is (as a function of time).

The unit of acceleration is particularly useful in making measurements, as we mostly use piezo-electric transducers (accelerometers) which produce a charge (voltage) that is proportional to the acceleration of the transducer.

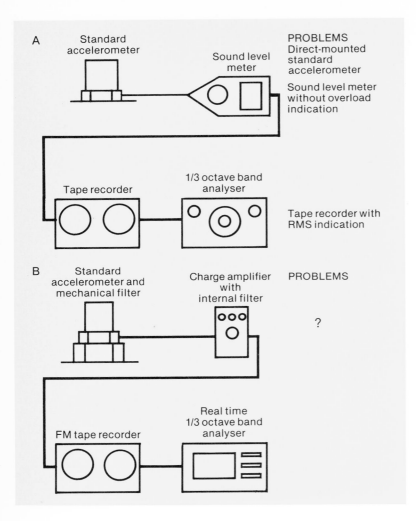

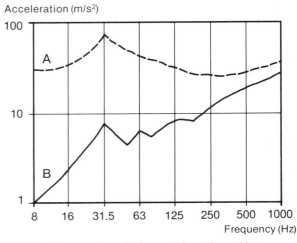

Different measuring chains and how they affect results.

The electrical signal from the transducer is processed in a charge amplifier and then passed on to an analyser or tape recorder.

The signal from the transducer sometimes contains not only signals describing acceleration of the object being measured, but also error signals created in the transducer due to intrinsic oscillation. The transducer mounting also affects the signal.

Hitherto, our measuring difficulties have largely been attributable to problems in identifying true and false measuring signals, and in passing the signal through the measuring instrument, without overdriving the amplifiers and thus further distorting the signal. Above we see two measuring systems and how they influence the results of our measurements.

The major measuring problems encountered by us are overloading of transducers and overdriving of amplifiers. The first problem frequently gives rise to the second.

The manner in which the transducer is mounted is of particular importance in measuring during work processes involving blows and jolts, i.e. in most measurements on hand-held tools.

Basically, the transducer problems arise because the piezo-electric transducer is a mass spring system with little internal damping (to increase the measuring range). The consequence is that the natural resonance of the transducer is easily excited during measurement in the process. High frequency input signals are considerably amplified (the transducer rings) and the output measurement signal from the transducer contains both measured signals and self-generated signals.

Even if we have sufficient dynamic range in our amplifier to process the total signal from the transducer, we will run into difficulties in distinguishing what is the measured signal, especially in the high frequency range. One method of avoiding ringing of the transducer is then to filter off the high frequency portion of the measured signal with a mechanical filter, before the signal enters the transducer. By so doing, the natural resonance of the transducer is not excited and in consequence we purposely limit our measuring range up to about 2000 Hz.

The method has been tested in PNEUROP SC17 with "back-to-back" measurements in a Round Robin test (see Vibrations in Pneumatic Hand-held Tools, Investigations on hand-held percussive tools) and elsewhere. This publication can be obtained from the "British Compressed Air Society, 8 Leicester Street, London WC2H 7BL, England".

As a result, we can now wholeheartedly recommend vibration measurements with a mechanical filter and with a charge amplifier with a large dynamic range.

Signal processing with frequency analysis and RMS-values

Our amplified signal describes acceleration as a function of the time. The high frequency content of the signal is reduced, which in physical terms means that rapid changes in the signal are damped.

The simplest and commonest way of processing this signal is to perform a frequency analysis, for instance in the 1/3 octave band, and to state a mean value of a varying RMS (Root Mean Square) signal. At this juncture we have separated ourselves from the physical process and it is becoming difficult to decide what our result actually signifies.

The reason for performing a frequency analysis is often that equipment is available for sound measurements. But noise arising from a machine is interpreted by the microphone as a composite signal from several sources and is experienced in a similar way regardless of the phase of the individual source. Vibration, on the other hand, is measured on a small surface and the physical significance is phase-dependent. Interpretation of a vibration signal is thus no easy matter.

The time function of vibration is the most pertinent description of the movement of the point of measurement, but it is difficult to describe this in units that can be compared from one point in time to another. At present, work is being done with different statistical units.

According to ISO 8041

Frequency	D	Frequency	D
0.80	36.00	100	15.91
1.00	31.99	125	17.93
1.25	27.99	160	19.94
1.60	23.99	200	21.95
2.00	20.21	250	23.96
2.50	16.05	315	25.97
3.15	12.12	400	28.00
4.00	8.51	500	30.07
5.00	5.27	630	32.23
6.30	2.77	800	34.63
8.00	1.18	1000	37.42
10.00	0.43	1250	40.97
12.5	0.38	1600	45.42
16.0	0.96	2000	50.62
20.0	2.14	2500	56.23
25.0	3.78	3150	62.07
31.5	5.69	4000	68.01
40.0	7.72	5000	73.98
50.0	9.75	5300	79.97
63.0	11.83	6000	85.97
80.0	13.83	10000	91.96

Filter characteristics for weighted values according to ISO 8041.

Weighted values

In recent years, we have started to carry out wide-band analyses in the form of weighted values. This means that the measuring signal is made to pass a weighting filter with a specified characteristic. The filter originates from ISO work which will be referred to later on.

If, after having passed through the filter, the signal is RMS treated, we obtain a single number which describes the vibration of the object being measured. This has numerous advantages when we wish to describe the vibration characteristics of a certain machine.

Unfortunately, there are several pitfalls in wide-band analysis. In fact, we have very little possibility of controlling the measurement process.

A frequency analysis does not only describe the level of the vibration signal in different frequency ranges, but also affords an opportunity to see whether or not measurement has been properly performed. For example, DC shifts (jump-like changes of the DC-voltage level interpreted in the frequency analysis equipment as an increase in the low frequency level or, if they are periodical, often as an increase in the basic frequency, e.g. in percussion machines), natural oscillations in the transducer, etc. can be revealed to anybody accustomed to reading analyses.

These errors cannot be detected in a weighted value reading.

A weighted value can also be calculated from a 1/3 octave band spectrum. In this case we use the attenuation figures from ISO 5349. The two methods do not necessarily give the same result, owing to differences in filter characteristics and tolerances, so a certain degree of discrepancy is always present.

Even though we can state the vibration properties of machines in weighted values in our sales promotion literature, product development calls for more informative methods of measurement and analysis.

Our figures will be related to international standardized measurement procedures, the reason being that the work process has a decisive influence on the level of vibration and that this must be described in detail. Otherwise, the value will be meaningless.

International standardization work

The injurious effect of severe vibrations on the circulatory system in the hands has been known since the beginning of this century, but no attempt was made to draw up any standards in this field until the 1960's.

In the Soviet Union, a hygienic standard was published in 1966 in which a definition was presented of what was meant by vibrating machines, with accompanying restrictions in time of use, feed force and calls for regular medical examinations and prohibition for juveniles to work with such machines. The Soviet standard has been followed by national counterparts in several countries of the Eastern Block and in Japan. These countries have viewed the vibration problem more seriously than the Western World, where attention has been paid above all to the ambient hygiene situation.

Towards the end of the 1960's, a working committee was formed within the international organisation for standardization (ISO), with the task of producing factual documentation for an appraisal of how vibrations influence man. Various research reports were also collected, among them Dr Miwa's investigations on perception and subjective experience of vibrations, which was to become a trendsetter.

The fundamental concept was that anything experienced as troublesome was in fact also harmful.

Vibrations on some different types of machines were measured, among them chain saws; and regular epidemiological examinations were carried out on the group of individuals who used the machine in question. The results were compared with the experience criteria.

The result showed that in test person groups with machines with vibrations greater than the level experienced as troublesome, there were more individuals with vascular changes than in groups working with low-vibration machines.

During the 1970's, several medical, engineering and epidemiological studies were performed with the aim of determining the level of vibration load to which human beings can be exposed without incurring injury.

Several attempts have been made to explain the arise of injury from mechanical action on the hands to biological changes in the vascular system, in the nerves and in the skeleton. No plausible theory has as yet been presented.

In the technical measurements, only the vibrations have been measured in the vast majority of cases. Parameters such as squeezing force and feed force have not been measured because of technical difficulties. A machine that requires high feed and squeezing forces will thus be assessed the same as a machine with low handle forces. Laboratory measurements in which handles have been mounted on a vibrator table, and the dynamic reaction of the hand to vibration studied, reveal clear differences in the transmission of vibrations to the hand at different squeezing and feed forces.

Medical experts have also run into problems when carrying out their investigations. A vibration injury is exceedingly difficult to diagnose at an individual level. The method reverted to after innumerable attempts with plethysmography, X-ray with contrast fluid, vibration provocation, cold provocation, skin temperature measurement, discrimination testing etc. is the individual's subjective story of his disease history.

Since injury frequently arises only after exposure for several years, the technical measurements must be supplemented with knowledge as to which machines were used by the sufferer over the years, their vibration data and the extent to which they were used.

For this latter reason, among others, most of the studies have been performed in the forest industry; where only one type of machine (the chain saw) has been used, where the exposure time can be calculated with a reasonable degree of certainty and where it is relatively simple to form control groups for the medical examinations in which the individuals included in the group have the same work situation, i.e. outdoor work with roughly the same burden and the same age composition.

These investigations have resulted in the compilation of ISO document 5349, which describes a dose-response relationship, i.e. how

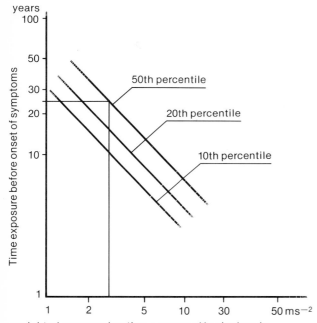

Dose — response relationship of vibrations in handles

$$a_w \, (T \ hrs) = a_w \, (4 \ hrs) \left(\frac{4}{T}\right)^{\frac{1}{2}}$$

$$a_w \, (4 \ hrs) = 3 \ ^m/_{s^2}$$

a certain daily vibration level given as a weighted value which, when affecting a group of individuals, gives rise to a probable percentage of injury within that group after a number of years.

Based on ISO 5349 the relevant industrial safety authorities in each individual country will draw up national standards.

The constant a_w(4 hrs) = 3 m/s² shall be seen as an example where 50% of an exposed population will have early symptoms of vibration disease after 25 years of exposure.

National recommendations, such as those of the American ACGIH give a figure a_w(4 hrs) = 4 m/s². It is likely that several countries will follow this approach. It is not very appropriate to use decimals in this constant because it indicates a numerical precision that we do not possess.

The work on national standards has started and hopefully we will achieve harmonization between different national standards to avoid barriers to trade.

It is important for machine manufacturers to be given an opportunity to successively adjust their product range to the development of standardized restrictions.

If the standard was to be introduced overnight, so to speak, we would be faced with the problem that virtually all hand-held tools including busily-used hammers would have a severely reduced daily time usage factor or be prohibited altogether.

All machines vibrate. There are simply no easy ways in which to reduce vibrations down to the levels that are considered to offer no risk when experienced for eight hours a day, day after day, year after year. In the best case the problem can be solved through total redesign, whereas in others we will be obliged to concentrate on changing the process or by significantly reducing the working hours per day.

Work with machine-measuring methods

The measurements which largely serve as a base for the mechanical engineering studies in ISO 5349 were performed during the 1960s and the early part of the 1970s. Present-day knowledge of the limitations of the measuring equipment used at that time is such that we occasionally question the validity of the results.

Since we became aware of the difficulties involved in accomplishing comparable vibration measurements, the question was raised within PNEUROP, the European Committee of Manufacturers of Compressors, Vacuum Pumps and Pneumatic Tools, and a working committee was appointed in 1974. The task of this committee was to study vibrations in hand-held pneumatic machines and to draw up standardized measuring methods. This working committee, which is known as Committee 17, has published two reports which deal with measurements on grinders and chippers. The reports can be ordered from the Maschinen-Verlag GmbH Lyoner Strasse 18, 6000 Frankfurt / M. 71 Germany.

Committee 17 commenced its work with a Round Robin test in which six laboratories performed vibration measurements on four grinders which were sent from one laboratory to another. Each machine had a milled plane with a threaded hole on the support handle for attachment of the transducer. The machines were tested without a grinding wheel, suspended in the air hose while idling. All machines had an idling speed, the rotational frequency of which was dominating, and which ended up in the 125 Hz octave band.

The mean values vary within a power of ten, owing to different production qualities. Vibrations in the most severely vibrating machines, however, are barely perceptible. The standard deviations show the dispersion obtained when measuring on this very simple and, above all, constant source of vibration.

The next test was aimed at determining how the vibrations were affected after fitting a grinding wheel on the machine. The four machines tested previously were now tested again by their respective manufacturers. As earlier, the machines were run at idling speed with different grinding wheels or with the same grinding wheel, which was removed and re-fitted prior to each test. (See table on page 77)

The conclusions that can be reached from the results are:

that the vibration level increases severely when idling with a wheel;

The measurements gave the following results:

Vibrations in 125 Hz octave band in m/s^2

	Mean value	Standard deviation
Machine 1	3.8	0.5
Machine 2	1.4	0.2
Machine 3	3.3	0.5
Machine 4	0.3	0.2

	Manufacturer 1	Manufacturer 2	Manufacturer 3	Manufacturer 4
Different grinding wheels	26.4±10.7 (12 wheels)	19.5±14.2 (10 wheels)	17.7±6.6 (10 wheels)	19.5±13.2 (10 wheels)
Same grinding wheel fitted several times	16 ±10.5 (10 fittings)	16.5±2.8 (10 fittings)	14.1±1.6 (10 fittings)	11.5±1.9 (10 fittings)

that the dispersion between different wheels is very great;

that the vibration level changes upon refitting the same wheel.

However, we did not succeed in predicting the vibration level through the change in fitting procedure (e.g. change in tightening torque).

The next question was: how do the idling vibrations change after grinding has been carried out for some time?

Virtually all tests show that the idling vibrations decrease after grinding for a short time, which suggests that the grinding wheel becomes worn in. The correlation between the level of idling vibration and the level of vibration during work, on the other hand, is weak. This is due to the fact that additional forces are now involved. Occasionally, the grinding wheel jumps and in consequence the contact forces become nil momentarily. This gives rise to shocks in the system (measurement problems).

As mentioned before, the Pneurop work has led to two test methods:

Vibration measurements on grinding machines.
Vibration measurements on percussive tools.

In the ISO TC 118 SC3 WG3, continued work is being carried out on drawing up "test codes" for several different types of machines. This work is arranged so that all information of a general nature is collected in one document which is then followed by a number of sub-documents in which special types of machines, e.g. grinders, chipping hammers, chisels, drills, percussion drills etc. are dealt with.

How can the influence of vibration be reduced?

If we disregard the possibility of reducing the exposure time, what remains to be done is to reduce vibrations in the handles. Personal safety equipment in the form of gloves has hitherto proved to have no appreciable effect. Reduction of vibrations usually means that a thorough analysis of dynamic forces in the machine and process must be performed. This force analysis is followed by a study in different mass spring systems. The theory of vibration damping is simple, but if we permit our directions of movements and rotations to expand into several dimensions, the theory can rapidly expand to uncontrollable proportions.

To be more practical:

Acceleration can be reduced by decreasing the force of excitation or increasing the effective mass. Acceleration can also be reduced through attenuation via a mass spring system.

Which of these possibilities can be applied to handheld machines?

The mass of a hand tool cannot be radically changed without having an unfavourable influence on the means of handling. Existing examples of an increase in the mass of the machine are heavy dollies in riveting, and those occasions in which rock drilling machines are loaded with extra weights.

In some cases, the force of excitation can be radically changed by redesigning the tools. Imbalance in rotating parts can be reduced or the internal forces balanced in machines with reciprocating pistons.

Attenuations of the parts of the machine actually held by the operator is theoretically possible in virtually all cases. Practical elaboration of a mass spring system, so that efficient reduction is obtained without any adverse effect on the ease of handling of the machine, nevertheless often proves to be difficult. The system is often required to be capable of transmitting large static loads at the same time as it has to attenuate low frequency vibrations. A riveting hammer, for example, requires a static feed force of 150 N (34 lb). The impact rate of the tool is 30 Hz.

The handle and hand correspond to a mass of 0.5 kg (1.1 lb). With a spring giving a natural frequency equal to half the frequency of the disturbance force, the static deflection will be 30 mm (1.2"). A riveting hammer with such a large static deflection is experienced as difficult to control. It is obviously possible to pre-load a spring so that a moderate deflection is obtained at a nominal static load, but on the other hand this implies that the attenuation is ineffective for feed forces that are smaller than the nominal feed force. In operation there are considerable variations in the feed force, which makes pre-loaded dampers less interesting for hand tools.

Design solutions
The range of vibration-damped hand tools marketed by Atlas Copco includes several examples of the previously mentioned possible solutions.

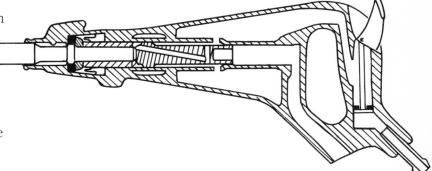

RRD-37 — a chipping hammer
The design goal was to reduce the oscillating force resulting from piston motion.

In the RRD series a differential piston moves in the cylinder. The supply pressure constantly acts on the rear surface. This pressure moves the piston forward. When the piston strikes the chisel, a volume in the front of the piston is supplied with air pressure, and because of the larger front area the piston moves backwards. The supply pressure is constant all the time. This means that the reaction force on the machine casing is always constant. This constant force does not give rise to vibrations in the machine housing. Shock reflections from the chisel to the front of the machine are absorbed by a chisel collet guided on the chisel. Two benefits have been gained in this design: a considerable reduction of the vibrations in the handle, and a simpler design without the valve system normally included in a percussion tool.

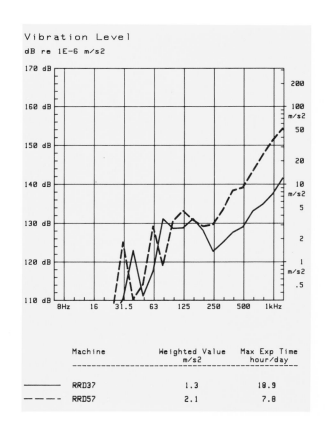

Machine	Weighted Value m/s2	Max Exp Time hour/day
RRD37	1.3	18.9
RRD57	2.1	7.8

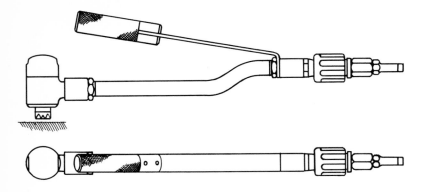

RPI — a scaling hammer
Despite the practical limitations previously mentioned, there are a few examples of vibration reduction through passive attenuation.

The RPI scaling hammer is the first usable tool with passive attenuation. The design is simplicity itself. It consists of a flat spring and a heavy handle. The system is weak to static loads but this is of minor importance in this case.

LSF 16 — a die grinder
Die grinders do not belong to the machine category that we normally characterize as severely vibrating.

These machines are, however, used for long periods of time, perhaps more or less continuously throughout the working day, so there is every reason to work further with vibration control.

Sources of vibration
The predominant forces influencing the mass of the machine come from imbalance in the grinding tool, and contact forces between the grinding tool and the material. Imbalance in the tool may occasionally be amplified in consequence of the rotor shaft becoming bent on account of rough treatment. The machines are delivered with a run-out that is less than 0.1 mm (0.004"), 12 mm (0.5") outside the chuck.

The dynamic contact forces between the grinding tool and the material are normally of the same magnitude as the static feed force imparted to the machine by the operator. These are desirable and control the stock removal rate of the grinding tool. If the grinding tool is out of

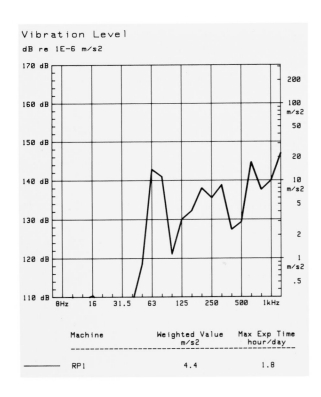

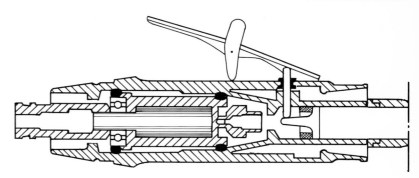

true, the dynamic contact forces may become greater than the feed force, which means that the grinding tool jumps on the workpiece, resulting in high vibrations in the machine. For grinding tools which consist of grains of abrasive in a bonding agent, the tool usually wears itself in towards lower out-of-trueness. In other words the vibrations in the machine decrease after it has been in use for a short time. The dynamic contact forces are periodical, with the same frequency as the rotational frequency. Since they are not sinusoidal, a frequency analysis reveals a fundamental frequency with a number of harmonics.

Design

The design requirements in this instance were to accomplish a rigid axial attachment in order to be able to secure the motor (not shown in the fig.) and a weak radial attachment to accomplish vibration isolation.

This was solved by allowing the motor assembly to rest against a spherical bearing in the leading edge, where the balls prevent axial motion but roll with low friction during radial movements. These are absorbed by a soft O-ring in the leading edge and a somewhat stiffer ring in the trailing edge. The motor assembly can thus be imparted a pendulating motion in relation to the outer shell. The coupling between the motor assembly and outer shell is low in the leading edge and higher in the trailing edge. Since the source of vibration is located at the front part of the motor spindle, the higher coupling in the trailing edge of the

machine does not constitute any major disadvantage.

The properties of the weak elements between the motor assembly and outer shell have been determined by vibrating the spindle on a vibrator table with known acceleration, while measuring the acceleration response on the outer shell. This enables the transmission properties of the suspension to be determined by comparing the input and output signals. What limits the weakness of the suspension is its ability to transmit feed forces.

Vibration data

The vibration properties of the machine are determined whilst working. Since vibrations derive from the process and practical die grinding consists of a multitude of processes with a large selection of different grinding tools, no unique data on vibration in the shell can be presented, especially as it would then also be necessary for us to perform measurements at a number of points on the shell in three directions. An attempt to arrive at a practical solution to this problem is nevertheless currently being made within ISO 118, where a standardized measuring

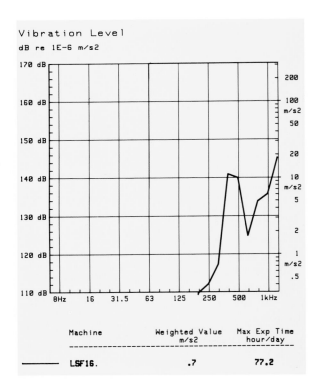

Machine	Weighted Value m/s2	Max Exp Time hour/day
LSF16.	.7	77.2

procedure is being drawn up.

The values presented here are average values from a large number of measurements in different common working situations.

Measurement is performed with the transducer located in the middle of the handle, and with the direction of measurement perpendicular to the ground surface.

Measurements of subjective experience
One aspect which we suppliers of machines most decidedly cannot disregard, is the subjective experience of a machine at work. It is by no means obvious that a machine which satisfies all the requirements imposed by the authorities when it comes to vibration, also actually feels better than one that does not satisfy these requirements. Subjective assessment of a machine rests on the impression of a host of factors, among them vibration.

The subjective experience of vibration can be investigated by permitting an individual to make pairwise comparisons within a group of machines, where we ask which one of the machines in the pair vibrates the most. We can also try to quantify the experience by allowing the test subjects to answer, say, the following question:

If one machine vibrates, for example, a hundred units, how many units does the other vibrate? By comparing a number of machines with one another, for instance 10 machines, we can draw up a relative scale which expresses a subjective experience of the machines. Human beings are very good at making comparisons and different individuals may rank a number of machines in a very similar manner.

Field measurements of our vibration damped machine performed by different research groups, have given results which agree with undamped machines, whereupon we have been asked the question as to what our vibration damping mechanism actually consists of.

The fact of the matter is that the primary sources of vibration for a die grinder at work are imbalance and non-geometric aspects of the grinding tool, as well as possible run-out of the rotor of a maltreated machine. A standard machine with little rotor run-out, good tool geometry and little imbalance can very well vibrate less than a vibration-damped machine with inferior tools.

In order to test this assertion we carried out the following tests. We took ten new LSF 16 die grinders and locked the vibration damping devices on five of them, so that the machines corresponded to undamped machines. We then milled the faces on four pairs of pins so that the imbalance of these pairs was increased. We checked that the run-out of the machines was within the tolerance limits. The pins were then mounted in a collet on the machine instead of tools, so that each pair of pins was mounted partly in a vibration damped and partly in an undamped machine. By this means five pairs were formed. The first had unmilled pins. The other pairs were mounted in a similar manner. We thus had 10 machines, 5 vibration-damped and 5 non-damped, fitted in pairs with 5 different imbalances.

The machines were randomly mixed and suspended in balancers, whereupon they were designated 0-9. All pair combinations were then randomly generated. The questionnaire contained 90 pair combinations and each test subject was tested twice. All in all, 10 test subjects were used.

The test was performed by a test leader who had the questionnaire and who could survey the machines, passed left 8 and right 2, for example, through a hole (see figure).

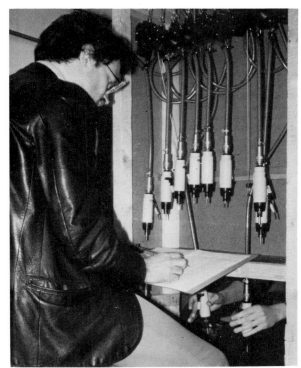

Test leader, following a questionnaire, gives different pairs to the testsubject.

The test subjects who saw the machines come down through the hole took one machine in each hand. They then ran them alternately and answered the investigator, say, left 70, which means that his left-hand machine is vibrating 70 in comparison with his right-hand machine which was vibrating 100. The answer partly contained an assessment of which machine was vibrating the least and an assessment of how much less it was vibrating.

A subjective scale has been calculated from this material, which comprises 1800 pairwise comparisons.

To arrive at an objective value with which to make a comparison, repeated vibration measurements were performed on the machines.

When the magnitude of the vibrations is to be presented along a scale, we wish to have one value, not a frequency analysis. We can, for instance, use a weighted value according to ISO 5349.

As evident from the graph, the results from the damped standard machine and the undamped machine are very close to each other in terms of subjective experience and vibration level respectively, in the case in which no imbalance was introduced. Now this may appear self- evident, i.e. if the vibrations in the rotor are small the vibrations in the casing will also be small, regardless of whether the machine is damped or not. With increased imbalance, however, we can see a decided difference between the standard machine and the non-damped variant.

Note that the vibration measurement values do not differ by more than about 10 dB between the highest and lowest value, which is less than specified in ISO 5349 as the limits for 1 hour and 8-hour exposures respectively. We have not, then, been working with extreme differences in vibration levels but have nevertheless arrived at a decided difference in subjective experience.

The next tests with the machines were performed during a typical work cycle. Six machines, three vibration-damped and three non-damped, were used. The machines were fitted with a wear top, a washer being placed between this and the machine. Washers 3 and 4, and washers 5 and 6, were provided with eccentric holes of pairwise different dimensions.

The test series was commenced and concluded by permitting the test subject to grind with all six machines, whereupon vibration measurements were performed. The vibration data or mean values of the results from these two measurements for each machine were recorded.

Pairwise comparisons were made between the six machines during grinding. Data processing was performed in the same manner as previously and the following results were obtained.

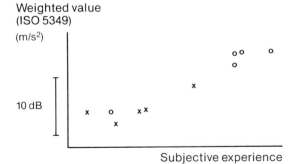

Weighted value
(ISO 5349)
(m/s²)

10 dB

Subjective experience

o Non-damped machine
x Standard machine (vibration-damped)

Pairwise comparisons with ten LSF 16 running free

Weighted value
(ISO 5349)

(m/s²)

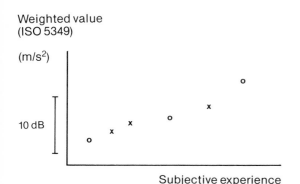

10 dB

Subjective experience

o Non-damped machine
x Standard machine (vibration-damped)

Pairwise comparisons with six LSF 16 at work

Weighted value
(ISO 5349)

(m/s²)

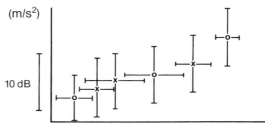

10 dB

Subjective experience

o Non-damped machine
x Standard machine (vibration-damped)

Pairwise comparisons with six LSF 16 at work

Once again we may state that it is fully possible to find a non-damped machine with lower subjective experience than a damped machine at low vibration levels, but if we compare a damped machine with a non-damped machine under vibrating conditions, a damped machine is always to be preferred.

The values presented in the graph are mean values. If we plot the spread in vibration values, the figure will adopt the following appearance:

For all machines, the objective spread is greater than 10 dB. In other words, when a machine has been operated by ten individuals in the same working situation, the spread of measuring data has exceeded 10 dB. The conclusion inevitably to be drawn from this is: that it is extremely difficult to assess the risk from limited measurement material. Each individual measurement must be regarded as

unique, unless enormous efforts have been made to keep different variables under control in a laboratory environment.

Elaboration of methods for standardized laboratory condition measurements will impose exacting demands on specification of work situation, measuring methods, signal processing and reporting of results if reproducible values are to be obtainable.

LSV 36 — an angle grinder
The LSF 16 die grinder has a number of successors in the form of the somewhat larger die grinders LSR 26 and LSR 36.

In cases when these are used as angle machines, the weak suspension of the spindle cannot be utilised on account of the angle gear in the front end of the tool.

As a rule the tool features a support handle

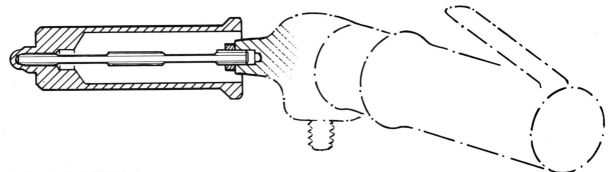

Angle grinder LSV 36

which protrudes at an angle of about 120° from the trigger handle.

The moment of rotary inertia of the tool along its longitudinal axis is low, implying that a rigid handle will have a high vibration level, particularly in the outer end, since the tool and handle move rigidly, i.e. in phase.

By introducing a mass-spring system in which a central pin comprises the spring and the surrounding handle the mass, vibration can be reduced. The pin has been designed so that the surrounding handle has roughly the same amplitude in both its inner and outer end. This design has been chosen rather than the alternative with a rubber-suspended handle, as the latter will be torsionally weak and therefore difficult to work with as precision is more difficult to perform.

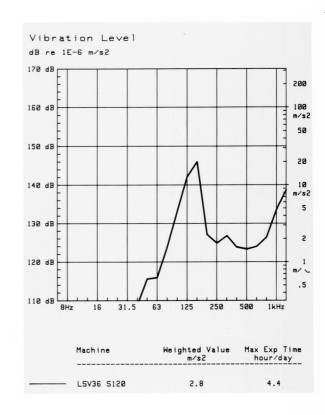

Machine	Weighted Value m/s2	Max Exp Time hour/day
LSV36 S120	2.8	4.4

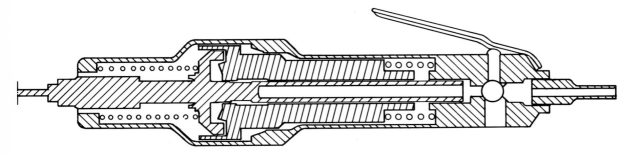

Scaler RVM 06

RVM 06 — a scaler

If welded joints are to be of good quality it is essential for all slag to be removed. A transition from manual scalers to a small chisel hammer has enabled welding to be speeded slightly, by working with higher current intensities, resulting in the formation of weld beads and burns, which can easily be removed with a chisel hammer. One undesirable side effect of this, however, has been a high noise level on account of the process noise and high vibration levels.

Some efforts have been made to return to the use of manual scalers or to use needle scalers in which the chisel is replaced by a bundle of hardened pins. This, however, has not received general acceptance. To counteract the side effects, a weld scaler has been designed.

Sources of vibration

The RVM 06 is not percussive in the sense that a shock wave from a piston strikes a chisel shank, causing high contact forces at the tip of the chisel and thus removing material. Instead, the oscillating piston of the machine is permanently connected to the chisel. Piston movement is accomplished by compressed air which drives the piston forward against the workpiece, and by a spring which drives the piston rearwards.

Design

To prevent reaction forces from the compressed air and spring setting the machine casing in motion, i.e. vibrating the casing that we hold in our hand, an additional mass spring system has been introduced. This system has the same natural frequency as the former one, but also oscillates in counterphase. When idling, the reaction forces of the two mass spring systems

Machine	Weighted Value m/s2	Max Exp Time hour/day
Scaler RVM06	2.1	7.4

on the machine casing will be equally large and opposingly directed. Consequently, no vibration occurs in the mass of the casing.

RRH 06 — a riveting hammer

In cases where high feed forces are to be transmitted to the workpiece via the machine, and where the inner dynamic forces of the machine cannot be easily counterbalanced, we are faced with a difficult design problem to solve.

The inner forces can only be prevented from reaching the handle of the machine if this is isolated with a soft mass spring system. If the feed force is to be transmitted via this soft mass spring system, it is essential for this to be pretensioned to the anticipated feed force level, i.e. inactive for lower forces and butt-compressed for higher forces than the feed force. There are few working situations in

which the feed force can be stated so precisely. As a rule, this varies from nil to what we can perform during a short time, i.e. approx. 500 N (100 lb). Pretensioned mass spring systems, therefore, do not afford an ideal solution.

Riveting is a precision task. In the aircraft construction industry, for example, the demands for a satisfactory result are completely indispensible and must be fully satisfied. The feed forces vary, depending on the location of the riveted joint in the structure and on the working posture.

Design
An active damping system has been designed to overcome the problems described above. The spring in the system consists of an air cushion, in which the spring constant is inversely proportional to the volume and directly proportional to the pressure. The transmittable feed force is directly proportional to the pressure.

The design functions in that when the machine is held against the rivet and a feed force is applied, a relative movement occurs between the cylinder and handle housing, where a bearing with low friction is located. When the cylinder is inserted into the housing, a servo-piston behind the cylinder and percussion mechanism is also activated. This servo- piston controls the pressure level in the air cushion at the rear of the machine. The machine responds to contraction via a pressure rise in the air cushion. This pressure rise enables larger feed forces to be transmitted.

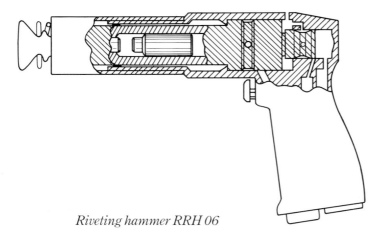

Riveting hammer RRH 06

When the machine is riveting, forces are generated due to shock reflexions from the riveting process as well as air forces to drive the percussion piston. These forces set the cylinder percussion mechanism and servo-piston in motion. Movement also occurs in the structure being riveted and this movement is also transmitted to the machine.

The durations in time of these movements are, however, so transient that they are filtered off in the slow mass spring system, which consists of the air cushion (the spring) and the handle housing (the mass).

One of the aims in dimensioning the damping system is to achieve a low natural frequency in order to filter off the vibrations from the process as effectively as possible. This dimensioning cannot be done unless the hand-arm system is included in the calculation model.

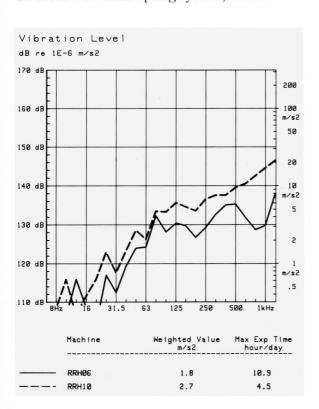

Summary

Several major environmental factors influence the operator in professional work with hand-held machines. Comprehensive work has now been going on for several years in an effort to obtain control over factors likely to have an injurious effect. Subjective experience is also an important consideration. Those factors that are to be weighed together give rise to optimisation problems that are difficult to solve.

All machines vibrate, often as a result of the production process in which they are used.

HOW TO DESIGN
dust controlled power tools

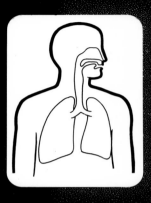

HOW TO DESIGN
dust controlled
power tools *by Erik Ahlberg*

HOW TO DESIGN
dust controlled power tools

The following is intended to provide an overview of dust and fume formation in connection with industrial material removal processes using hand tools, to illustrate how dust affects people, and to show how to reduce the emission of dust from hand tools.

Fundamental definitions

The air we breathe contains the basic components, oxygen, nitrogen and minor amounts of carbon dioxide and inert gases, but also gaseous and particulated pollutants.

These latter substances can occur in both solid and liquid form and can vary in size. A large amount of particulate floating in a bearing medium is called a dispersion. When the bearing medium is air, the dispersion is known as aerosol.

A fixed aerosol contains solid particles which, when they are larger than 0.5 μm (1 μm = 1/1000 mm = 0.00004 inches) are called dust and when they are smaller, smoke. Dust is normally created by the mechanical finishing of materials while smoke is the product of incomplete combustion.

An aerosol containing droplets of liquid is called fog when the size of the droplets exceeds approx. 0.5 μm and smoke when the droplets are smaller. The droplets can be formed when, for instance, a liquid is dispersed during, say,

spray painting or lubrication of pneumatic tools. It is also formed through vaporization resulting in condensation such as during combustion, welding and brazing.

Respirable dust

Of all the dust particles contained in aerosol, those considered to be most dangerous are those between 0.1 μm and 5 μm in diameter. These particles have the ability to follow inhaled air into the deepest inner cavities of the lungs, the alveoli, and remain there even if the majority are exhaled again. This dust is termed respirable, or inhalable.

It is in the alveoli that gas exchange takes place, the body emits carbon dioxide and takes up oxygen. That's why it is so important to ensure that the alveoli do not become covered with dust or damaged by aggressive dust particles.

In assessing the danger posed by a particular aerosol, it is important to know how much respirable dust the aerosol in question contains. So, samples are taken, usually using a preseparator which separates the non-respirable dust and allows the respirable dust to pass through to the sampling equipment.

At an international conference held in Johannesburg in 1959, the following specifications were laid down for the separating characteristic of a preseparator for spherical particles with a density of 1 g/cm^3.

Particle dia. (μm)	% that passes the preseparator
1.6	95
3.5	75
5.0	50
6.1	25
7.1	0

In addition to the specifications of the "Johannesburg Convention" which are applied in Sweden and other countries, similar specifications are used in the USA, developed by the ACGIH (American Conference of Governmental Industrial Hygienists).

Drop velocity

In discussions concerning dust separation, it is of interest to establish the drop velocity of the particles.

For example, for spherical particles with the density of water, 1 g/cm^3, drop velocity in air at a temperature of 20 °C is:

dia.(μm)	drop velocity (cm/s)
1	0.003
5	0.07
10	0.3
50	7
100	30

However, since spherical particles are only present in aerosols containing droplets of liquid, the expression "drop velocity" equivalent diameter has been introduced for solid particles. This is the diameter of a spherical particle having the density of water, which drops just as fast as the particle in question.

The table illustrates that respirable dust remains floating in air longer while larger particles drop fairly quickly.

How are people affected?

The protective mechanisms of the respiratory system

When we inhale an aerosol, some of the particles will be separated. They first pass through coarse filtration in which the air passes the hairs in the nostrils. The uneven walls and curved passages of the nose cavity force the air to keep changing direction. This tosses the heavier dust particles against the moist mucous membranes where they get stuck, a process known as impaction. In addition, once inside the nose, the air becomes warm and moist. The particles that get stuck in the front section of the nose are blown out, while the particles that get stuck farther in are carried to the gullet by the motions of the mucous membranes, and swallowed. As the dust continues through the air passages in the lungs further impaction takes place. The passages branch out and the diameter decreases. Some sedimentation occurs, when the air passages become so narrow that even smaller particles have time to sedimentate despite their low drop velocity. In addition, some of the particles are carried towards the walls by means of diffusion (equalization of concentration).

Air passages exceeding a cross sectional diameter of 1 mm are covered with a mucous membrane. This is made up of cells carrying fine protoplasmic processes (cilia), and of mucous-producing cells. As the cilia are in constant motion, a wave action is induced in the mucous layer which causes the particles that have been deposited to be transported upwards.

Air passages with a cross section below 1 mm do not have any mocous-producing cells, and when the diameter is below 0.5 mm (0,02") there are no cilia either.

The tiniest air passages end in globular expansions, the alveoli, where the gas exchange takes place. The walls of the alveoli are covered with a thin skin containing a dense capillary network. The walls also contain cells called macrophages which have the capacity to absorb particles of dust. After having absorbed a particle of dust, the macrophage is dislodged from the wall of the alveoli and moves like an amoeba towards other adjacent dust particles which are also absorbed. After some time the macrophage dies, since it no longer receives any nutrient support. It is transported away by the air movement in the alveoli (Expiration is faster than inhalation).

Some dust particles penetrate the wall of the alveolus and are transported away by the blood and lymphatic systems. Others get stuck and cause reactions of different kinds.

This goes to show that our respiratory mechanism is highly complex and easily disrupted. For instance, infections can kill cilia cells and mucous cells over large surfaces, which then reform once the infection has passed. Initially, tobacco smoke boosts the function of the cilie, only to impede it over a longer period which hinders the removal of foreign particles. It is also likely that tobacco smoke impedes the activity of the macrophages.

Inert dust

Most of the dust we inhale is harmless or inert. In other words, its only effect on the body is that it covers a certain surface of the inner area of the lungs which would otherwise be used for gas exchange. This means that inert dust is a burden for the body as it makes breathing more difficult and the dust must also be conveyed from the lungs as described above. "You get heavy-chested," as one worker in a marble quarry once said.

The usual limit on the permissible level of inert mineral dust is $10mg/m^3$ of air, but the level of respirable mineral dust is set at $5 mg/m^3$.

Dust that affects the function of the lungs

Most of the cases dealt with here are fairly dated and describe phenomena that exist only in exceptional circumstances today. But this can be regarded as an explanation for the existence of hygienic threshold values and a reason why they shouldn't be exceeded. These phenomena are broken down into groups below according to the most commonly occurring.

1. Dust from certain metallic compounds such as manganese, vanadium, cadmium, beryllium and others can give rise to severe inflammation of the lung tissues, a condition not unlike pneumonia, varying naturally in degree of seriousness depending on the degree of exposure and the type of dust involved. A relatively mild form is known as zinc ague which is caused by zincoxide.

2. Certain types of dust can give rise to excessive sensitivity.

3. Dust from asbestos, chromates, radioactive substances, arsenic and nickel can, over a long period of exposure, give rise to lung cancer.

4. Some substances when occurring as dust can generate the formation of fibrous tissue in the lungs rendering them inflexible and nonelastic. The most dangerous substances are silica, asbestos and talcum while less dangerous substances include mica and kaolin. This group can also be augmented by beryllium and cobalt. Silica, which causes silicosis is especially dangerous. Descriptions of this disease can be found in ancient writings. Newly-crushed silicon dust which sticks in the lungs causes the formation of tiny fibrous nodules of connective tissue which eventually grow together reducing the capacity of the lungs. Silicosis cannot be arrested, growing progessively worse. The greater the exposure to silicon dust the faster the illness progresses. Nevertheless, the incidence of silicosis has been greatly reduced thanks to years of persistent preventive work and is today relatively uncommon.

An especially hazardous silica dust is formed from quartz that has just been violently smashed. Thus, road dust is fairly harmless in this respect.

5. Some forms of dust exist in the form of tiny fibres e.g. asbestos. There is a connection between the structure of the fibres and the biological effects of the particles. (Fibres in this context, are defined as particles with a length/diameter greater than or equal to 3). Fibrous and tumour causing effects stem from fibres longer than $10\mu m$. The fibrosis-causing effects increase with increasing diameter while the tumour-causing effects seem to be confined to fibres thinner than $0.5 - 1.5\ \mu m$. Fibreglass fibre appears to be inert.

Dust that is resorbed

The dust from a number of substances penetrates the wall of the alveolus and is carried out in the lymph system. These substances include, for instance lead and cadmium, which can give rise to intoxication symptoms and which can only be removed from the body very slowly. Most of the tiniest particles of otherwise unsoluble substances can be resorbed and carried away.

Hygienic threshold values

The hygienic threshold value is defined as the maximum acceptable mean level (time-weighted mean value) of a substance contained in breathing air.

Most industrial countries have listed threshold values for known, dangerous industrially-occurring substances. A comprehensive list of about 400 substances has been issued in the USA by the ACGIH. If a particular substance does not appear on the list, it is possible to obtain an idea of its hazards by examining the toxicological data.

Considering the fact that about 5000 new product substances are developed every year, which are either used individually or in combination with other substances or as additives, then it is fully justifiable to call for caution in using a new substance, if its composition and the effects of its component parts are unknown.

To cite an example; during the grinding of steel a type of dust is generated that also contains the alloy substances of the steel. Depending on the type of steel, the dust could contain chromium, nickel, vanadium, tungsten, manganese, titanium, cobalt, beryllium etc. which often occur as carbides. The grinding disc generates dust made up from, e.g. aluminium oxide, zirconium oxide, silica carbides, boron nitride, and from the binder comes phenolic plastic, ceramics and bronzes.

Additive effects

If the dust contains several substances each one of which is potentially dangerous, it is possible to estimate their aggregate degree of hazard. From the following condition:

$$\frac{C_1}{G_1} + \frac{C_2}{G_2} + \frac{C_3}{G_3} + \cdots + \frac{C_n}{G_n} \le 1$$

where C_n is the concentration of the respective substance

G_n is the threshold value of the respective substance

can be determined if they, together, are too dangerous and which of them it would be most profitable to reduce.

In addition to this, one must also take into account the synergistic effect, or the fact that one substance can amplify the effect of another. Tobacco smoking is an example of a factor which can strengthen the effects of an array of substances. In other words, all industrial operations must be run in a manner that prevents anyone from being subjected to hazardous exposure to any substance. This can be done by adhering to three different principles:

1) Preventing the spread of hazardous substances by conducting a given process in a booth and in a vacuum atmosphere.

2) If hazardous substances still spread, set up secondary ventilation to drive the level of the substance in the breathing zone far below the hygienic threshold level.

3) By furnishing personal protection equipment during for instance repair work, when other safety equipment is disconnected.

Measuring dust content in the breathing zone with a mobile unit.

How is dust measured?

The filter method

It is important to be able to measure the level of dust in the air, and in particular the respirable particles. Through the years, a number of measurement methods have been developed based on a variety of principles. The method that has proven to be the most effective, giving the greatest benefits, and which has become predominant, is the "filter method".

The advantages of the filter method are:
   a) It is easy to obtain overall amount, size distribution and chemical analysis from the same material.
   b) The dust can be collected during a single work shift providing a mean exposure value for that shift.
   c) The equipment is compact and lightweight and can easily be carried around, attached to clothing.

The method is simple. An air pump draws air through a filter which separates the dust. The flow of air passing trough the filter is roughly the same as our average flow of inhaled air during the work shift. The level of dust in the air is calculated by dividing the weight of the dust with the amount of air. This figure can be directly related to the hygienic threshold value.

Direct indicating instruments

It is highly advantageous to have access to a direct-indicating instrument as this eliminates the often time-consuming evaluation work. If the test computations are complicated and several people are directly involved in the testing, it is an obvious advantage to be able to assess the measurement results quickly, make adjustments or modifications and then continue the testing.

With non-stationary conditions in which test data changes while the test is in progress, the only way of obtaining detailed information of the process is with a direct-indicating instrument, since the quantities of dust usually involved during the short test periods are too small to be measured using the filter method.

Nevertheless, it must be emphasized that a direct-indicating instrument cannot replace the filter method, because the results are not absolute but relative and cannot be given in mg/m^3 unless the instrument is calibrated with respect to the dust being measured. Furthermore, there are still no direct-indicating instruments available that are small and light enough to be fastened to a worker's shoulder. Therefore, they can usually not be used for measurements where results will be compared to hygienic threshold values.

Photo-optical gauges

These types of gauges are based on the Tyndall effect, i.e. light distribution around a particle. The aerosol to be analyzed is drawn through the instrument by a suction device. A light beam is directed through the aerosol and the stray light is measured with a photo meter. The reading gives a relative measure of the dust content.

Several instruments make use of this method. One of them is the TM Digital made by Leitz and originally designed for monitoring the dust content in coal mines.

Since the measured value is a measure of the light distribution of the aerosol, the instrument gives no indication of the absolute quantity of dust in the aerosol. On the other hand, it is an excellent means of measuring relative values. To achieve absolute values, the instrument must be calibrated by carrying out measurement in parallel with the filter method.

The calibration value applies for dust with the same light distribution, density and particle distribution. The last factor can be regarded with a certain reservation for two reasons.

To begin with, the instrument as a source of light, utilizes a light emitting diode which generates infrared monochromic light with a wave length of 0.94 μm. As a result, the instrument performs the largest part of its measurement in the respirable range (fig. 1).

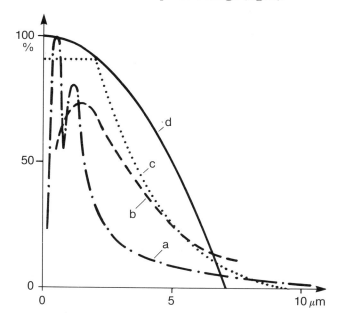

Fig. 1. Respirable dust. Particle distribution according to different criteria:
a. Analysis sensitivity for TM Digital
b. Alveoli deposition
c. According to ACGIH
d. According to the Johannesburg Convention

Consequently, the particle distribution of coarser particles is of no interest.

The second reason is that the instrument may well carry out measurements in the respirable range but its characteristic deviates from that of the Johannesburg Convention. The latter describes instead the pre-separator used upstream of the filter in connection with the calibration measurement. At a constant respirable particle distribution, the difference is of no significance, but at a varying particle distribution the result can be affected. If the instrument is to be used for performing absolute measurements, detailed information on the dust to be measured is required. As this knowledge exists for most industrial environments, then this requirement need not be a problem. The TM Digital is one of the larger instruments available, while the RAM-1 from GCA Corp is one of the smallest, although it is, in some respects, more advanced than the TM Digital.

Particle counters

These instruments also make use of the Tyndall effect, although in a somewhat different manner. The aerosol is drawn in through a beam of light at a rate determined by the dust density. Each particle then gives rise to a flash of light the intensity of which is dependent on its size. The light is detected by a photo multiplicator. In this way, both the number of particles and their size can be established.

ß-absorption meter

The aerosol is drawn through a glass filter strip which collects the particles, or the particles are obtained by means of impaction on a piece of plastic. Thus a test sample is obtained which is subjected to radiation. Sample absorption of the radiation is directly proportional to the sample mass, regardless of the substance. The remaining radiation is measured in a detector (ionization chamber) the outlet voltage of which is reversely proportional to the mass of the dust.

The amount of mass is directly readable in mg/m^3. Each test lasts for more than one minute.

Piezo electric meter

The aerosol is drawn through a charging chamber in which the particles are given an electric charge. A piezo electric crystal acts as a collector and the particles are deposited on its surface. The crystal is induced to oscillate at its resonance frequency. Fluctuations in resonance frequency provide a measure of the dust mass deposited on the surface of the crystal.

Another form of gauge collects the charge from particles that strike the detector, and then measures the current from the detector, which is a measure of the deposited mass.

Test methods

Machine measurements

Type testing
There is still no standardized method of measuring dust emissions from machines, which is why there is no method for comparing the properties of machines in terms of dust emission. Admittedly, machine comparisons have been conducted, but each of them is unique because they cannot be performed again elsewhere and give the same result.

Comparative machine measurements should be performed to provide buyers with some form of proof of performance. Should a machine demonstrate a particular characteristic in a carefully specified test in a given typical work process, it is reasonable to expect that essential portions of that same characteristic will appear in on-the-job conditions. If two machines generate different values for the same characteristic in the same test, then this difference will carry over in similar actual work conditions.

It is not certain, on the other hand, that the machine will come up with the same values as during the test, simply because conditions such as temperature, wind, material and so on are entirely different. So, standardized machine measurements would provide the information needed to select the best machine for a given job, although it is impossible to predict what the actual on-the-job result would be.

One of the major difficulties in developing standards is that the work process must be characteristic for the tool, and yet idealized enough to enable it to be performed anywhere in the world. The work material must be easily available, the set-up simple, and the entire method inexpensive.

In situ testing
Conducting machine measurements on a worksite is a part of the way to improve working conditions on the site with respect to dust emissions, such as by changing the extraction nozzle position or capacity, trying out other types of tools and so forth.

It is these types of measurements which suit direct-indicating instruments the best. They tell you immediately whether a particular change has improved conditions. As is the case for all measurements of this kind, many measurements must be taken in series in order to minimize the effects of the random spread of the measurement results.

The Tyndall effect can also be utilized in order to illustrate the amount of respirable dust and to make a quantitative assessment of whether the steps taken have had the intended results. This method is depicted in the diagram on the next page. An intense light beam is directed through the area where heavy dust build-up is suspected. This shows up the respirable dust as indicated in the figure, provided that the eye is shaded against the direct light from the lamp.

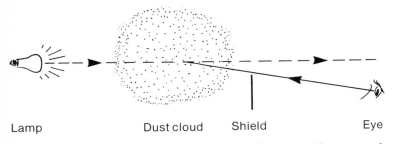

Lamp   Dust cloud   Shield   Eye

Fig. 2. Respirable dust can be illuminated by means of a strong beam of light.

In addition, all other background lighting should be dampened as much as possible. Naturally, some background dust is also visible but it is usually fairly easy to distinguish from the dust being studied.

Measuring the health hazard

This type of measurement generally involves only measuring the total amount of dust in the breathing zone, to determine whether the level of dust has exceeded the hygienic threshold values for the substances contained in the dust. The filter method is used to achieve an absolute value of the concentration of dust and to determine its chemical composition. The measurements can be of varying length depending on the purpose of the test. For instance, they can be done for an hour or in stages to ascertain dust exposure during a given work process. The measurement may be made for a period of hours, or throughout an entire work shift to determine a worker's total exposure to dust, or during work with a certain machine to study the effects of modifications to the machine or the work process. The measuring procedure is described in detail in several other reference works.

Methods for reducing dust in air

Three obvious, concise rules for lowering the level of dust in the air we breathe will be discussed.

Preventing the formation of dust

Since dust is the product of mechanical finishing treatment, preventing its formation would seem to be virtually impossible. Nevertheless, there are an array of processes that can utilize water flushing so that all particle formation takes place under water and where the particles do not come in contact with air until they are fully agglomerated.

Examples of such processes are rock and concrete drilling as well as certain types of grinding, diamond cutting and so on.

Collecting dust as close to the source as possible

This is done chiefly by means of fitting dust extraction devices on tools, such as dust extraction hoods around drills or grinding discs. This works extremely well in some cases while in others it may be totally inadequate and alternatives must be sought. The first alternative to be considered is to position the workpiece in an enclosed work bench where it is accessible through an opening. In addition, an extraction device is fitted to induce a steady flow of air through the opening into the box. Spray from the machine is aimed inwards. Instead of a box, a work bench could be used, furnished with extraction openings in the surface to permit a flow of air to blow through in a downward direction. Movable spot extraction is also suitable with nozzles shaped like funnels positioned in front of the spray. These nozzles can be suspended by balancers and fitted with attachment magnets or suction cups to enable them to be detached and moved around easily. This would be a suitable solution for repair work for which it is difficult to maintain a permanent work site.

The second alternative is that the entire work site is enclosed and supplied with extraction equipment and sufficiently powerful general ventilation. As a result, the rest of the premises housing other, non-dust-forming activities can manage with a normal ventilation rate. If these measures still do not produce an acceptable work environment, then the worker must be furnished with personal protective equipment.

Cleaning

Keeping a workplace clean and free from a build-up of dust helps eliminate secondary dust, which is dust that has already settled and is swirled up again to settle somewhere else. Tools should be stored in cabinets above the worksite instead of being spread out all over work benches and pallets. Protective equipment not being used should be stored in a cupboard away from the actual work site.

In many cases, it may be advisable to vacuum off workpieces that have been finished before they, as secondary sources of dust, serve to spread the dust to other areas of the premises.

Fig. 3. Air can be blown a distance corresponding to 10 times the blow diameter, before the velocity in the beam has dropped to 0.1 times the blowing velocity. For extraction, however, velocity at a distance corresponding to the diameter of the inlet opening is only 0.1 times the extraction velocity in the opening.

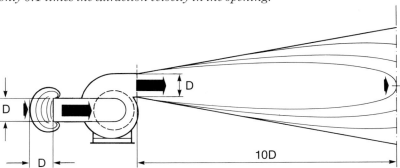

Fig. 4. The grinding spray from a grinding machine can cover a 45 degree sector from the grinder.

Dust extraction systems

Dust extraction hoods

Grinding machines
The spray from grinding operations spreads from the point of contact between the grinding disc and the material, in the direction in which the disc is rotating and in a sweep of up to 45 degrees.

The larger particles are propelled straight forward in a tangential direction while particles smaller than 10 μm swing off in the rotation direction of the disc. The smaller the particles the more they swing off in the rotation direction.

Fitting an extraction hood over the disc, either fixed or rotating with the disc, permits the extraction of mainly the smallest dust particles. It is essential that extraction takes place immediately adjacent to the periphery of the disc as the dust follows the disc around. Thus the flow of air being sucked towards the extraction opening can work upon the dust for a comparatively long time. Another method is to extract the dust through holes in the grinding disc.

There are a number of different cover designs

depending on how the machine will be used.

On a sander equipped with a support disc and abrasive paper, an early design is a hood fitted over the disc and rotating with it. A number of spacer pins are placed between them. Since both are flexible, when the disc is pressed against the workpiece it bends, after which the hood bends correspondingly, maintaining a constant suction gap. Fig. 5.

The edge of the hood has a lip that is folded down over the edge of the disc to act as a mechanical grinding spray shield. Most of the spray is then swept up by air that leaks in between the hood and the workpiece. The drawback here is that the lip prevents grinding in corners. To resolve this, another hood is available without the folded lip. The fine dust that follows the rotation of the wheel, is drawn up into the gap while a lesser amount of coarse particles are captured. Fig. 6.

This was not found to be a fully satisfactory solution for all types of work, so an alternative was designed where the hood was mounted permanently onto the machine and furnished with a bent-down edge in the form of a brush, or a plastic edge with an opening along the front. By positioning the point of contact between the wheel and the workpiece close to where the wheel passes in under the hood, most of the dust and particle spray is sucked up. This latter design retains the good visibility of the earlier design but also has improved suction in the area in which the spray is formed. Selecting the proper design is a matter of preference depending on the job in hand. Fig. 7.

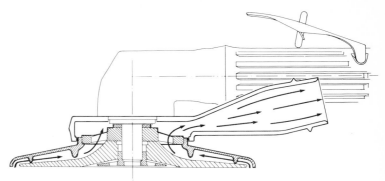

Fig. 5. Extraction hood with bent-down lip for fibre disc.

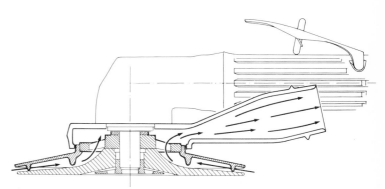

Fig. 6. Extraction hood with straight lip for fibre disc.

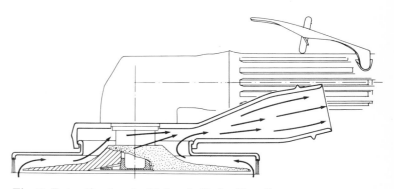

Fig. 7. Extraction hood with brush-lip for fibre disc.

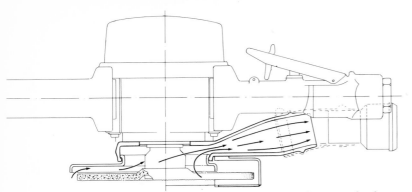

Fig. 8. Extracion hood for a depressed centre wheel.

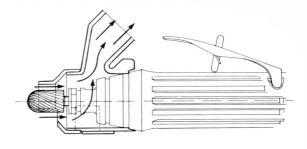

Die grinders are equipped with a plastic enclosure with a front opening.

The same basic principle is used on grinders with depressed centre wheels. In this case, the hood is designed like the peak of a cap, protruding from the disc behind the contact point with the workpiece. The bent-down edge of the peak is much closer to the upper side of the grinding wheel bringing about an extraction opening at the front edge of the wheel. This design works very efficiently for fine dust but much of the coarser dust escapes.

Straight grinders are equipped with a short shield immediately in front of the spray. While the tool is working, the shield moves against the surface. The shield is made of aluminium so that the spray of coarse particles that is blown up against it, cakes into a mass that can easily be removed by lightly tapping the cover.

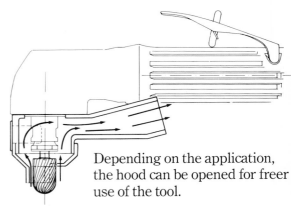

Depending on the application, the hood can be opened for freer use of the tool.

Fig. 9. Extraction hood for a straight grinding machine.

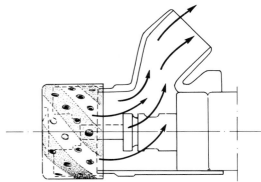

For diamond-tipped grinding drums, the drum cavity is connected to the suction extraction system. Holes have been made in the periphery through which the dust is drawn into the tool.

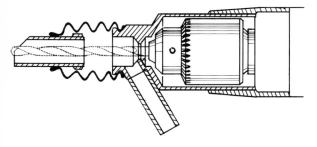

Fig. 10. Drilling machine with extraction hood.

Drilling machines

The drill is completely covered and the hood is pressed against the workpiece to be drilled. When positioning the drill, the hood can be pulled back, to improve visibility and then pushed forward when drilling starts.

When drilling upwards it is especially important to use the hood as all dust will otherwise fall out into the air.

It is also particularly important to use a hood for drilling in carbon-fibred materials with electrical machines, as carbon fibres may enter the machine and cause short circuiting.

Chipping hammers

It is not easy to apply dust extraction for chipping work because:

a) the size of the pieces removed varies widely, especially during concrete chipping. Large pieces can clog up the extraction opening or prevent extraction of the fine dust hidden behind them.

b) the chisel penetrates the workpiece making it difficult to position an extraction hood close to the dust generation site,

c) the hood is subjected to heavy mechanical wear when pinched between the tool and workpiece. As usual in complex situations, a compromise has been reached. The hood is a relatively flexible rubber hose through the centre of which the chisel protrudes. The length of the hose can be adjusted to the job in hand with a knife. Owing to the flexibility of the hose it is continuously adjusted to both chisel and workpiece and the opening is directed towards the dust source.

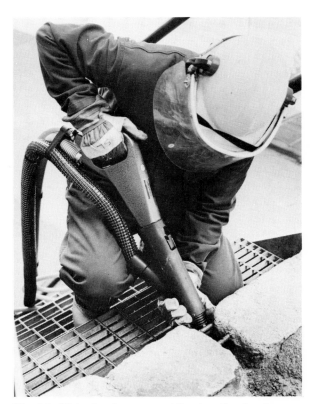

Fig. 11. Chipping hammer with extraction hood.

107

Suction hose

The suction hose is one of the most important components in a dust extraction system. It determines the ease of operation of the system but is also the component which produces the biggest pressure drop in the system.

Pressure drop and ease of operation are two contradictory parameters and the final choice is always a compromise.

The extraction hood requires a given rate of air flow to achieve sufficient inlet speed for efficient extraction. There are mainly two factors that determine pressure drop. One is the diameter of the hose and the other is the length. One must always be aware that every increase in hose length causes a considerable deterioration in suction efficiency. A solution is to begin with a thin hose close to the machine and then increase the diameter when the hose is supported by a swing arm. The suction hose and air hose must be clamped together using special rubber strips to make the system as easy as possible to handle.

Fig. 12 indicates that when a flow of 200 m³/h (7060 cubic feet/hour) is flowing through the extraction hose, we get a pressure drop of 1800 mm (71") w.g. in a 5 m (16.4 feet) length of 1.5" hose. If we further assume that the extraction hood, transport lines, filter etc, give rise to an additional pressure drop of 500 mm (19.7") w.g., we must use a vacuum unit with a capacity corresponding to 200 m³ per hour (7060 cubic feet/hour) at 2300 mm (90") w.g. If the 5 m hose is too short, a combination of a 3 m 1.5" hose and a 7 m 2" hose will give about the same

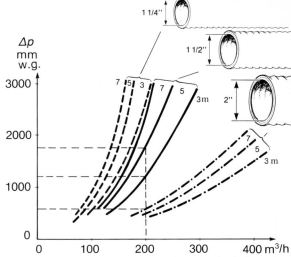

Fig. 12. Pressure drop —flow diagram depicting various hose diameters and hose lengths. The hose is a spiralreinforced suction hose.

pressure drop. With a longer suction hose than is technically feasible, the vacuum system will not work properly and the user will not be satisfied with the suction performance.

Swing arm

The suction hose should be supported by a swing arm. This is the best way to keep the hose off the floor and avoid stepping on it. This is important, as a deformed hose produces a much higher pressure drop at the same flow than an undamaged hose. A coiled hose also produces a higher pressure drop than a straight hose.

The swing arm illustrated can carry a 2" hose. The end with the connector hangs down to the work position where it is coupled to the machine. The short suction hose is connected to the air hose and is permanently fixed to the machine. The only disadvantage with this system is that the machine and hoses together take up more room if they are to be stored away in a locker at the end of a work shift. This problem has been solved on many worksites with a special tool board where the machines can be suspended. This helps keep things tidy and makes a more pleasant workplace. And because it is efficient it boosts productivity. It makes maintenance easier as it is simple to see which hoses need replacing. This is particularly important, as a poorly maintained extraction system is not efficient.

Vacuum valve
Dust extraction systems are often designed with more extraction points than the vacuum unit can handle, if all are used at the same time. For this reason, only the extraction point in use should be connected. Therefore, the design parameters of the systems are based on statistical considerations. The machine is connected to the system by means of a vacuum valve. This valve is regulated by the air flow to the hand-held machine, and automatically opens the vacuum line when the machine is in use.

Pipe work
There are two rules of thumb which are used when determining the size of transport pipes. The minimum requisite velocity to prevent dust from settling behind bends is about 10 m/s (33 feet/s). The maximum acceptable velocity with respect to pressure drop is about 40 m/s (130 feet/s). Usually we use three extraction points per branch of pipe.

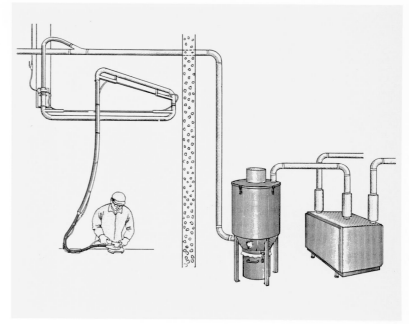

Fig. 13. A stationary dust extraction facility consisting of a tool with dust extraction, swing arm, pipe work, dust collector and vacuum source.

The ideal pipe size is 4" for horizontal main pipes. For larger facilities the system should be calculated on the basis of the probable number of simultaneous operations. These calculations become highly complicated since every change in the system changes the working point of the system (see fig. 27). If these calculations are made with a computer, it is easy to see the consequences of a change.

If the system must include long transport distances, it might be advisable to include a cyclone for coarse particles downstream of the extraction points. The pipe downstream of the cyclone can then be larger, which reduces pressure drop thereby reducing the load on the entire system.

Separation of dust from air

Cyclones

Cyclones are efficient for separating coarse dust particles. In a cyclone (fig. 18) the aerosol is sucked in tangentially at high speed and rotated downwards. The particles are then propelled against the wall of the cyclone by centrifugal force and moved downwards towards an emptying mechanism. The cleaned aerosol is extracted from the centre of the cyclone after having been relieved of the largest of the particles.

Filters

Many different types of filters may be used depending on the environment in which they are to operate. They may have to meet various requirements such as high operating temperatures, different types of chemical resistance, low moisture absorption, or electro-static charging.

A filter does not separate particles by acting as a sieve but primarily through impaction against the fibres of the filter, and from the fact that the air flowing through the filter gives it an electrostatic charge which attracts the particles to the filter material. The particles gradually build up to form a cake on the surface of the filter, which acts as a sieve. Depending on the type of dust, the porosity of the filter cake is reduced when the pores become clogged with particles and the pressure drop across the filter increases.

This increase can occur up to a certain level, in other words until the airflow through the filter and extraction hood is reduced to a point where it no longer functions satisfactorily. The filter must then either be cleaned or replaced. Whichever method is chosen will be a question of cost and safety. When cleaning the filter it will be necessary to use cleaning methods such as, vibrating or back blowing of the filter, so that the cake of dust particles loosens and falls down. The dust then has to be disposed of in a safe way.

For small installations, the least expensive method is to change the filter, and this is also the best solution if the filter simultaneously functions as a container for the dust.

Vacuum sources

Fans

In smaller systems, specifically mobile systems, fans are often used in order to create a vacuum. These are side channel fans and single- or multi-stage radial fans. When choosing a fan the characteristics of fans as illustrated in fig. 14, should be studied. These are usually supplied by the manufacturers.

The information is sometimes restricted to the intersections of the curve and the axes, i.e. maximum vacuum and maximum flow respectively.

This characteristic is sometimes approximated by a straight line between the two points (drawn in fig. 14). Note that these two points represent two extreme values that do not occur simultaneously.

The intersection of the curve with the p-axis shows the vacuum that is obtained when the flow through the fan is nil, i.e. when the inlet is closed. However, it is not certain that the lowest possible vacuum is then obtained. The pressure can, for example, follow the dotted line when the flow is so low that the air circulates around in the fan, possibly causing a certain amount of air to flow backwards.

In practice, however, this situation is irrelevant. The intersection between the curve and the flow-axis gives the maximum amount of flow the fan can give when the pressure difference across it is nil, i.e. when the opening

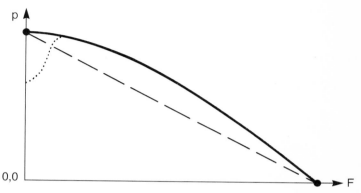

Fig. 14. Fan characteristic for a radial fan. p is pressure difference relative to atmospheric pressure and F is flow.

of the fan is fully open. In practice, zero difference is not obtained as there is always a certain amount of pressure loss in the intake and outlet of the fan. Other points on the curve (drawn with a solid line) are obtained at varying degrees of throttling in front of the intake to the fan, i.e. so that the inflow conditions are not affected. Fig. 15.

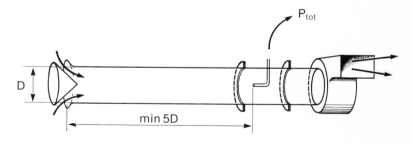

Fig. 15. Radial fan with a measuring section connected directly to the fan intake. A throttling cone is inserted in the intake.

Roots pumps

In larger installations where it is perhaps necessary to work with higher vacuum, a suitable Roots pump is chosen. As the Roots pump transports a certain volume with each revolution, it has a different characteristic from that of a fan. Let us imagine that the pump rotates at a certain rotational speed and without load i.e. p = 0. A certain amount of air flows through the pump. When the load later increases i.e. the vacuum increases, the air is thinned out in the volume which passes the pump i.e. the volume flow through the pump follows the perfect gas equation.

Fig. 16. Characteristic for a Roots pump without a leakage valve.

The load on the drive motor of the Roots pump is increased correspondingly. The motor is chosen to drive the pump at a certain maximum vacuum. The pump is therefore equipped with a leakage valve at the intake, which opens and allows air to leak in when a certain vacuum occurs. In this way the vacuum is limited when the pump is running and no vacuum valves are open.

Dust separation units

Pressure drop — flow characteristics

It is not only the characteristic of the vacuum source which typifies a dust separation unit. Once installed, the inflow conditions are not ideal as there is always a certain pressure drop in couplings, guide vanes, cyclones and filters. (Fig. 17.)

This reduces the maximum flow through the system. Even the position of the measuring section affects the flow, albeit to a lesser degree.

The pressure as a function of flow for the container etc. can be included in the diagram together with the fan characteristic as in fig. 18. The intersection point for the curves shows that the system without a filter being installed gives a maximum flow F_0 which is in fact less than the maximum that the fan can give, and that the intake pressure drop is p_0. The illustrated pressure drop is changed only by altering the design in a way that influences the flow conditions.

Fig. 18 shows the two components of the pressure drop. Line a represents, at a certain flow F_1, the pressure drop obtained from the permanent installations which are incorporated in the system in front of the fan. Line b represents the pressure drop which is obtained by throttling at the intake.

In an integrated dust separator unit it is the

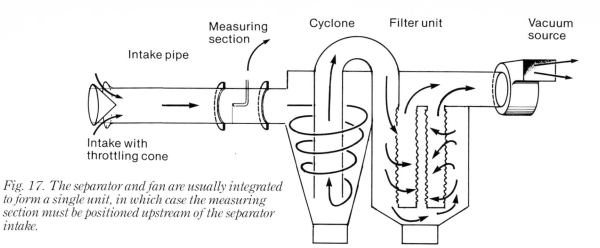

Fig. 17. *The separator and fan are usually integrated to form a single unit, in which case the measuring section must be positioned upstream of the separator intake.*

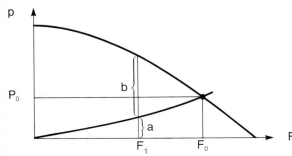

Fig. 18. *Pressure drop - flow characteristic for the fixed section of the separator. At a given flow, a corresponds to pressure loss in the separator while b corresponds to the available vacuum at the intake.*

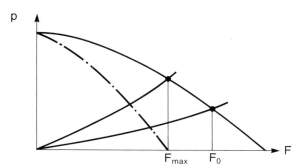

Fig. 19. *Pressure drop - flow characteristic for the fan and separator with filter, produces the maximum flow through the facility, F_{max}.*

complete installation including the filter which is of interest.

The flow characteristics of the filter cannot be assumed to be linear but to have a pressure drop - flow curve similar to that in fig. 18.

It is added to the previous curve in fig. 18 and a curve is then obtained which gives a pressure drop - flow curve for the complete dust separator unit, fig. 19. The point at which it intersects the fan curve is where the maximum flow through the system is obtained, F_{max}.

As a starting point for further discussion it is, however, advantageous to subtract this from the fan curve. This new curve, the dotted line in fig. 19, is called the system characteristic and shows the qualities of the system characterized at the point of connection, which is where the dust separator unit is connected to the rest of the system.

From the points discussed so far, one can draw the conclusion that the fan curve alone is not a sufficient measure of the characteristics of a dust extraction system, but that the entire system must be measured or analyzed.

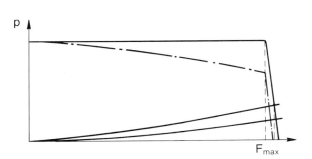

Fig. 20. *The system characteristic for a Roots pump is not as steep as that for a radial fan.*

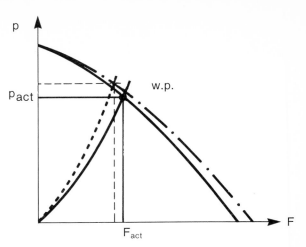

Fig. 21. *The point of intersection of the pressure drop - flow characteristic for the extraction hood - suction hose, and the system characteristic, is termed the working point. Its position indicates the actual flow in the system.*

The system characteristic in fig. 19 should be regarded as a mean value. The pressure drop across the filter is of course not constant but increases as the amount of dust on the filter builds up.

Immediately after a filter has been cleaned, the pressure drop is at its lowest and increases gradually as the dust cakes build up. This also means that the degree of separation provided by the filter increases during use. A completely new filter has lower pressure drop and lower degree of separation than a filter which has been in operation for some time.

By using a Roots pump, equipped with a leakage valve at the pump, a considerably straighter system characteristic curve is obtained than for a system with a fan.

The system working point

If an extraction hood is connected to the intake pipe it can be symbolized in the diagram by drawing in the pressure drop of the hood - hose as a function of the flow through them, as shown in fig. 21. The point at which the curve intersects the system curve determines the actual flow F_{act} for this system combination.

p_{act} is then the actual pressure drop obtained for a certain extraction hood and hose as far as to the extraction point.

The pressure drop - flow curve for the extraction hood and hose can be measured or calculated with the aid of information from the manufacturer concerning different hose lengths and diameters. This can be called hose characteristics. The intersecting point with the system characteristic is called the working point w.p. This gives the operating data that the system will have. If for example, the pressure drop for the extraction hood, should increase or the length of the suction hose is extended, the hose characteristic will move towards a higher pressure drop and lower flow, indicated by the

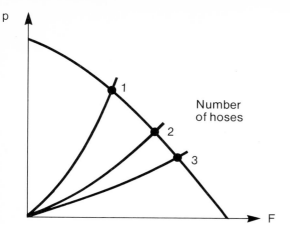

Fig. 22. *If several extraction openings are used in a system in which a radial fan is the vacuum source, the flow per extraction opening will drop substantially for each additional opening connected.*

dotted line in fig. 21. The transported dust will also force the hose characteristic towards the dotted line as the total pressure drop of the hood and hose increases.

The system characteristic is a mean value, of the positions of the working point which will move along the hose characteristic depending on the condition of the filter. If the filter has recently been cleaned the working point will be above the point drawn in the diagram. We then obtain a more powerful vacuum at the connection point because the pressure drop across the filter is reduced, and consequently we get a higher flow through the filter. This corresponds to the system characteristic for a cleaned filter (the dash-dot curve) so in praxis the working point moves around the point that has been marked in fig. 21.

If the system has been designed to serve several machines at the same time, it will also have several extraction openings. For

simplicity's sake, we can assume that all extraction openings perform equally. Depending on how many hoses are in operation at the same time, a range of hose characteristics is obtained, fig. 22.

The working point is shifted for each additional hose which is connected to the system, and for each additional hose the flow and pressure drop decreases in all hoses, even if the total flow increases.

A Roots pump in a system with several extraction openings functions as follows (see fig. 23): If curve A represents one activated vacuum valve at the connecting point, the flow through the system can be read off at the intersection point between curve A and the system characteristic. If curve B represents two activated vacuum valves we see that the flow is slightly less than doubled. The second vacuum

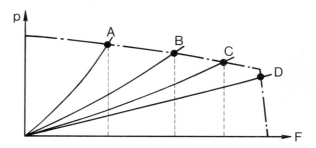

Fig. 23. *Several extraction openings in a system in which a Roots pump serves as vacuum source.*

valve is located somewhat further upstream in the system, so the hose characteristic must be amended to allow for the pipe length between the extraction point and the connection point. For curve C which represents three vacuum valves the flow is further reduced. Allow curve D to represent four vacuum valves. The hose characteristic now intersects the system curve at a point where the pressure drop is so low that the leakage valve is closed, which means that the flow has decreased substantially and we get a reduced flow at all extraction points. extraction points.

A minor alteration in this area produces a major alteration in pressure drop, and it is difficult to predict the total working point of the system as the curve falls so sharply.

The hose characteristic should not be used uncritically. The technical data contains information on straight hoses, which provides a basis for calculating the hose characteristic. However, if the hose is coiled, it will give a considerably higher pressure drop than the straight hose.

When designing systems, information is required first and foremost about which flow is required by the hoods, as well as whether all hoods or only a certain number of them can be presumed to be in use at the same time. With this information, the hose characteristics can be calculated and the working point established. The next question is whether the intended system can achieve the working point with a sufficient margin for filter clogging and for the dust capacity of the system.

Applications

Portable units

As an example we have chosen a ProVac P 55. This has been equipped with a 5,5 kW motor which drives a side channel fan. In an unloaded condition this can give a maximum flow of 530 m^3/hour. With a covered intake it produces a vacuum of 3300 mm (147") w.g.

The dusty air first enters a cyclone where the larger particles are separated. These are

Portable unit. ProVac P 55.

collected in a plastic bag which is housed in a metal container in the bottom of the separator. The partially-cleaned air is further cleaned in the filter unit in the upper part of the separator. After that it is sucked through the fan and ejected upwards. If need be, the separator can be equipped with a microfilter which is mounted on the exhaust from the fan. Thus equipped, the M4 is ideal even for separating asbestos fibres.

The filters are cleaned by blocking the intake to the cyclone which builds up maximum vacuum in the separater. With a lever in the upper part, a valve is opened which lets in the ambient air. This creates an airflow backwards through the filters that breaks away the dust cakes from the filter surface. To facilitate cleaning after being used for asbestos, the machine is very easy to dismantle.

Stationary installations

The suction source in a stationary installation is the advantageous Roots pump, which has a capacity specified that is relatively independent

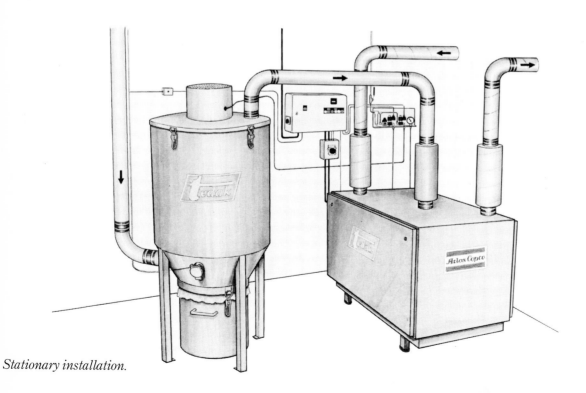

Stationary installation.

of the number or size of the extraction openings it is to serve.

From the extraction hood, which can either be permanently mounted on the machine or transferable spot extraction units, the dusty air goes through a coupling device with low pressure drop through a flexible hose to a swing arm. The purpose of the swing arm is partly to increase the system's reach and partly to keep the extraction system out of the way, above the activity level, as well as reduce the effort of handling the hose. The swing arm can also be complemented with a balancer. The bends of the swing arm system are rounded with large radii in order to reduce wear and pressure drop. At the base of the swing arm there is a vacuum valve which shuts off the pipe when that part of the suction system is not used. The valve will open automatically at machine start-up. Naturally it can also be manoeuvred manually.

From the valve, a wide bend leads into the main pipe towards the dust separator unit. There it passes a primary cyclone, a folded primary filter and a fine filter, after which the air is blown out through the Roots pump and an auxiliary silencer.

The filter part is equipped with a mechanical cleaning device and a container for the separated dust.

Two different grinders illustrating how the fine dust is sucked up into the dust extraction hood.
Next page. Grinding in a car repair shop. Note the overhead swing arm suction installation.

ALPHABETICAL REGISTER